Workbook A

Level 4

Siegfried Engelmann
Susan Hanner

A Division of The McGraw·Hill Companies

Columbus, Ohio

Illustration Credits

Rick Cooley, Susan Jerde, Heidi King, Simon Galkin, Paul
Montgomery, Den Schofield, Jim Shough, and Jessica
Stanley

Photo Credits

104, 110, 112 ©Corbis

SRA/McGraw-Hill

A Division of The McGraw-Hill Companies

Copyright © 2002 by SRA/McGraw-Hill.

Send all inquiries to:
SRA/McGraw-Hill
8787 Orion Place
Columbus, OH 43240-4027

Printed in the United States of America.

ISBN 0-07-569144-2

2 3 4 5 6 7 8 9 DBH 06 05 04 03 02

Name _____

A

1. What's the name of geese that are all white? _____

2. What's the name of geese that are gray and black and white?

    _____

3. Both geese and ducks are water birds, but _____
   are a lot bigger.

4. You can tell male geese from female geese because ▮▮▮ .

    • male geese have brighter colors
    • male geese are larger
    • male geese have longer feathers

5. What color are all geese when they are born? _____

6. How old are geese when they mate for the first time?

    _____

7. After male and female geese mate, they stay together ▮▮▮ .

    • for the summer   • for a full year   • until one goose dies

B   **Story Items**

8. Most geese live for about _____ years.

9. How old was Old Henry? _____

10. What was the name of the lake the flock stayed at during the summer?

    _____

11. In which season did the flock leave the lake? _____

12. In which direction did the flock fly? _____

13. How far was the flock going? _____

14. Who didn't want to make the trip? _____

15. He said that he was too _____ to fly so far.

16. What will happen to Big Trout Lake during the winter?

_____

Name _____

A

1. Make an **R** on Big Trout Lake.

2. What country is the **R** in?

   _____

3. Make an **F** on Crooked Lake.

4. Which lake is farther north?

   _____

5. Make a **Y** next to the lake that freezes in the winter.

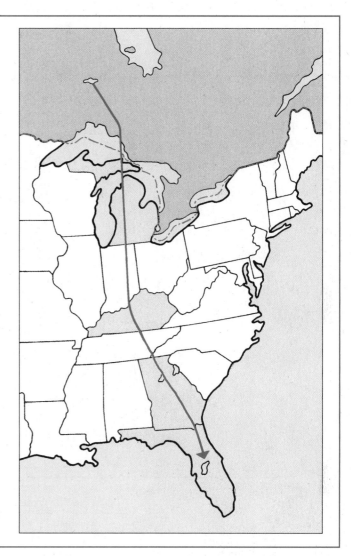

6. Geese live in large groups called _____.

7. In what country are most wild geese born? _____

8. Where do these geese spend every summer? _____

9. In which direction do the geese fly in the fall? _____

10. What is this trip called?

   • mating   • migration   • hibernation

11. Why do the geese leave Canada in the fall?

- There is no snow.
- The lakes freeze.
- The flock needs to fly.

12. Every fall, Old Henry's flock went to the state of ________.

B Story Items

13. Henry first mated with his wife when they were both ________ years old.

14. Henry's wife had died ________ years ago.

15. How had Henry felt ever since she had died?

- free
- tired
- lonely

16. After the flock had been gone for ________ days, Henry saw another goose.

17. Was that goose **old** or **young?** ________

18. The goose told Henry, "I couldn't learn to fly because ____."

- my leg was hurt
- my wing was hurt
- I was too small

19. When geese learn to fly, do they start **in the water** or **on the land?**

____

20. They run with their ________ out to the side.

GO TO PART D IN YOUR TEXTBOOK.

Name _____

A

1. Write the directions **north, south, east** and **west** in the boxes on map 1.

2. In which direction do geese migrate in the fall? _____

3. In which direction do geese migrate in the spring? _____

4. Make a line that starts at the circle on the map and goes north.

5. If you start at the circle and move to the number **4**, in which direction do you

   go? _____

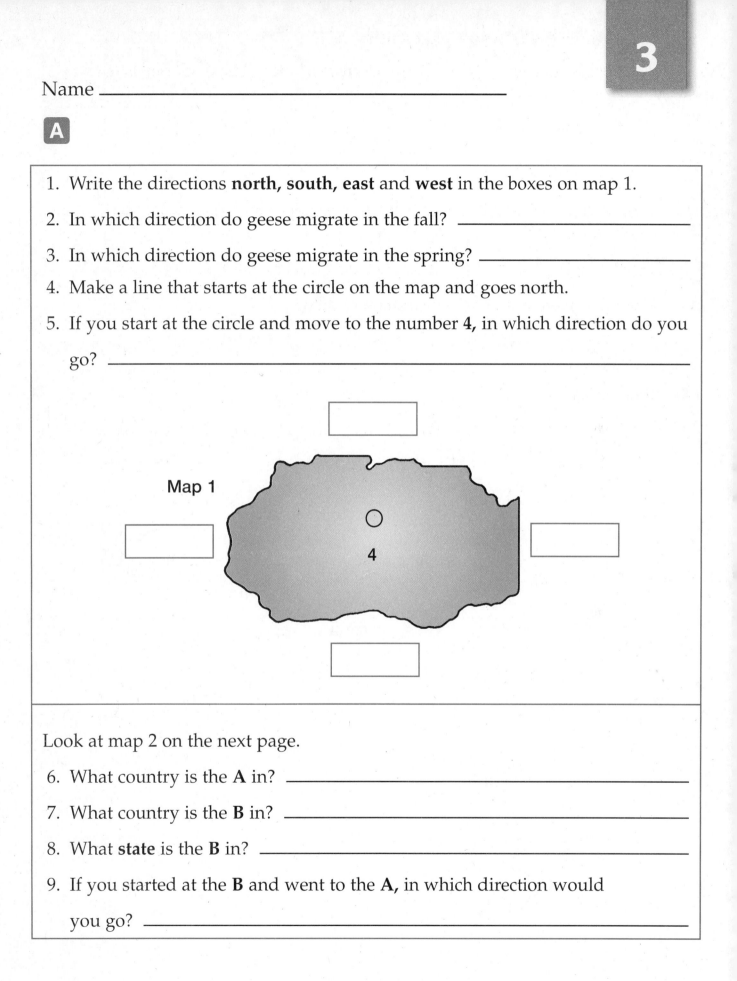

Map 1

4

Look at map 2 on the next page.

6. What country is the **A** in? _____

7. What country is the **B** in? _____

8. What **state** is the **B** in? _____

9. If you started at the **B** and went to the **A**, in which direction would

   you go? _____

Map 2

B Story Items

10. What was the name of the young goose? _____

11. When was that goose born? _____

12. How old was he?

    • more than a year   • less than half a year   • more than half a year

13. When young geese learn to fly, they hold their wings out as they ▆▆▆.

                • walk   • run   • swim

14. Tim couldn't learn to fly because he couldn't _____.

15. Was his leg still hurt? _____

16. **Underline** the 2 things that Henry said he would do for Tim.

    • show him how to stay warm   • build a warm house for him
    • fly with him to Florida   • tell him how to get to Florida
    • teach him how to fly

GO TO PART D IN YOUR TEXTBOOK.

6   *Lesson 3*

Name _____

A

Look at the map below.

1. What's the name of the place shown by the letter **A?** _____

2. Which letter shows the coldest place? _____

3. Which letter shows the hottest place? _____

4. Which letter is farthest from the equator? _____

5. The earth is shaped like a _____.

6. The hottest part of the earth is called the ▮▮▮▮.

   • pole   • desert   • equator

7. What's the name of the line that goes around the fattest part of the earth?

   _____

8. What's the name of the spot that's at the top of the earth?

   _____

9. What's the name of the spot that's at the bottom of the earth?

_____

10. The _____s are the coldest places on the earth and the

_____ is the hottest place on the earth.

11. How many poles are there? _____

12. Are the equator and the poles **real marks** on the earth or **pretend marks?**

_____

13. The farther you go from the equator, the ▮▮▮▮ it gets.

     • colder   • fatter   • hotter

B **Story Items**

14. Henry taught Tim to fly. Tim was supposed to run down _____

and hold his _____ out to the side.

15. What was Tim supposed to do when Henry honked?

_____

16. Did Tim take off the first time he tried? _____

17. Did he keep on flying? _____

18. Why? _____

19. Did Tim do better the second time he tried? _____

20. How high did the geese fly? _____

21. Where did they land? _____

22. Who was going too fast when they landed? _____

GO TO PART D IN YOUR TEXTBOOK.

Name _____

A

Choose from these words to answer each item:

• moon	• Florida	• equator	• geese
• poles	• Canada	• migration	• sun

1. The heat that the earth receives comes from the _____.

2. The part of the earth that receives more heat than any other part is the

   _____.

3. The parts of the earth that receive less heat than any other part are called the

   _____.

B **Story Items**

4. How many days did Tim practice flying? _____

5. When Tim flew in the direction that felt best, in which direction did he fly?

   _____

6. How much of the lake was frozen by the end of the third day that Tim
   practiced?

              • almost all   • half   • all

7. How much of the lake did Henry think would be frozen by the next

   morning? _____

8. Was Tim able to understand what Henry explained about the landing

   places? _____

9. How many landing places are there on the trip to Florida? _____

10. The first landing place is a field next to a _____.

11. That landing place has _____ on it.

Skill Items

The horses became restless on the dangerous route.

12. What word tells about how you get to a place? _____

13. What word tells how you feel when you want to do something different?

_____

Review Items

14. In which direction do geese fly in the fall? _____

15. What is this trip called? _____

16. In which direction do geese fly in the spring? _____

17. Write the directions **north, south, east** and **west** in the boxes.

18. Make a line that starts at the circle on the map and goes east.

19. If you start at the circle and move to the number **3,** in which direction do

you go? _____

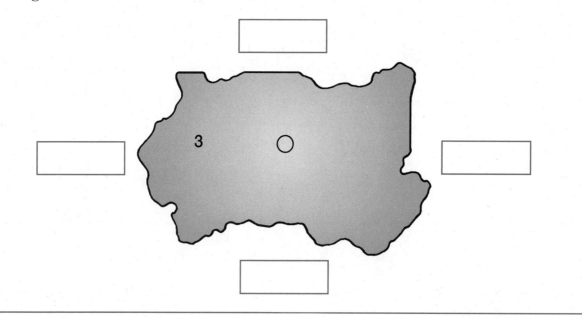

GO TO PART D IN YOUR TEXTBOOK.

Name _____

1. The sun shines ▮▮▮ .

   • some of the time   • all of the time

2. Can you see the sun all day long and all night long? _____

3. If you can see the sun, you are on the side of the earth that is ▮▮▮ .

   • closer to the sun   • farther from the sun

4. If you can see the sun, it is ▮▮▮ on your side of the earth.

   • nighttime   • daytime

5. What is it on the other side of the earth? _____

Look at the picture.
6. Shade the part of the earth where it is nighttime.

7. Which side of the earth is closer to the sun, A or B? _____

8. Which side of the earth is in nighttime? _____

9. Which side of the earth is in daytime? _____

10. The earth turns around one time every _____ hours.

11. Write the letter of the earth that shows the person in daytime. _____

12. Write the letter of the earth that shows the person 6 hours later. _____

13. Write the letter that shows the person another 6 hours later. _____

14. Write the letter that shows the person another 6 hours later.

_____

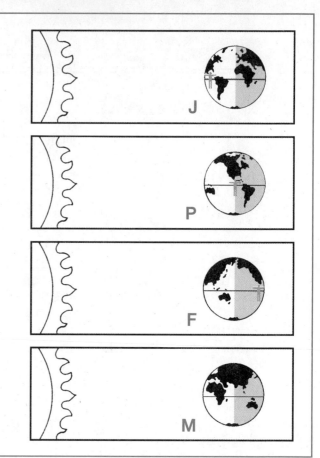

15. Which letter shows the place that has the warmest winters? _____

16. Which letter shows the place that is closest to the equator? _____

17. Which letter shows the place that is closest to a pole? _____

18. Is the **North Pole** or the **South Pole** closer to that letter? _____

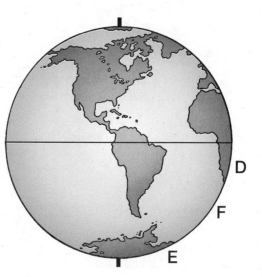

GO TO PART D IN YOUR TEXTBOOK.

Name _____

A

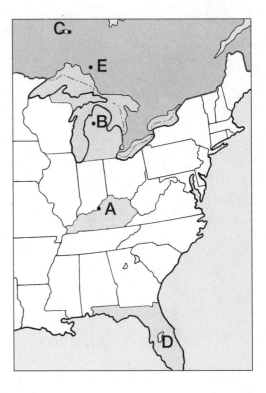

1. Which letter on the map shows Big Trout Lake? _____

2. Which letter shows the landing place in Kentucky? _____

3. Which letter shows the landing place in Michigan? _____

4. Which letter shows the landing place in Florida? _____

5. Which letter shows the landing place in Canada? _____

6. Which letter shows Crooked Lake? _____

7. Which letter shows the first landing place? _____

8. Which letter shows the second landing place? _____

9. Draw the path the geese take on their migration south.

B   **Story Items**

10. Did Henry tell Tim about his sore wing? _____

11. He got a sore wing when he fought with _____.

12. Henry told Tim about the next landing place. He also made a ▬▬▬.

    • mess   • map   • story

13. Did Tim recognize the next landing spot? _____

14. So what did Henry do?

    • led Tim to the landing place   • told Tim how to get to the landing place

15. **Circle** the picture that shows the correct landing spot.

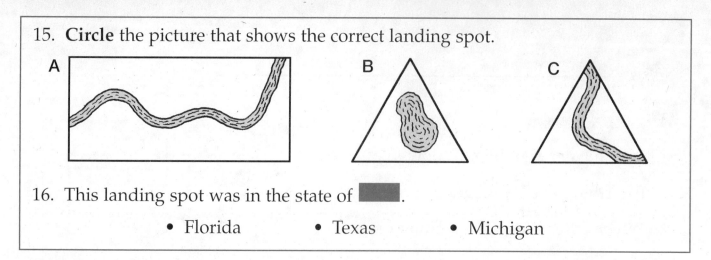

16. This landing spot was in the state of ▮▮▮.

    • Florida   • Texas   • Michigan

17. Was Tim able to tell Henry how to get back to the first landing place?

_____

18. What did the two geese see on the second day they were at the triangle-shaped field?

_____

19. Was that flock going to **Florida** or **Mexico**? _____

20. When Tim and Henry left Big Trout Lake, Henry had planned to take Tim to the first _____ landing places.

21. Now Henry realized that somebody would have to fly farther with Tim. How far? _____

22. Was Henry sure that he would be able to fly that far with Tim?

_____

GO TO PART D IN YOUR TEXTBOOK.

Name _____

Story Items

1. How many Great Lakes are there? _____

2. Color the Great Lakes on the map.

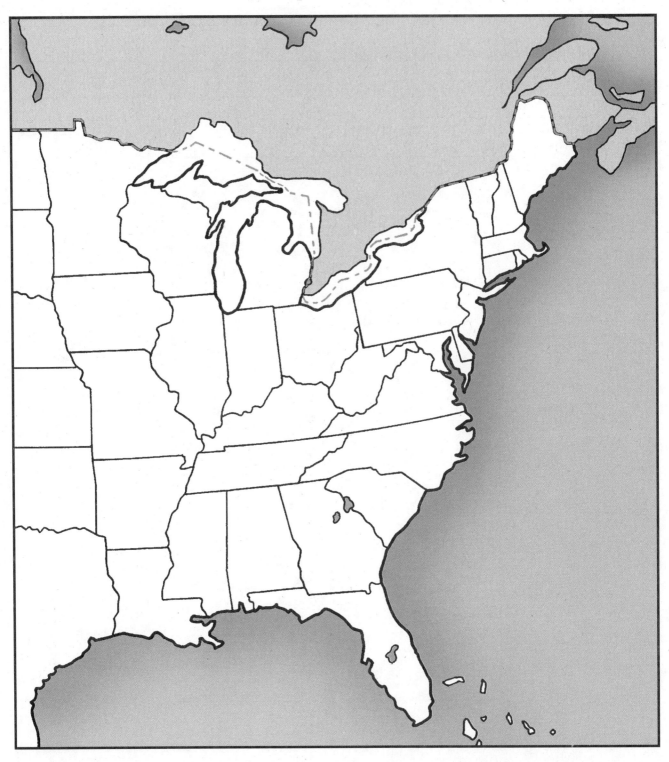

Review Items

3. Which letter on the map below shows the landing place in Kentucky? _____

4. Which letter shows Big Trout Lake? _____

5. Which letter shows the landing place in Michigan? _____

6. Which letter shows the landing place in Canada? _____

7. Which letter shows the landing place in Florida? _____

8. Which letter shows Crooked Lake? _____

9. Which letter shows the first landing place? _____

10. Draw the path that the geese in Henry's flock take on their migration south.

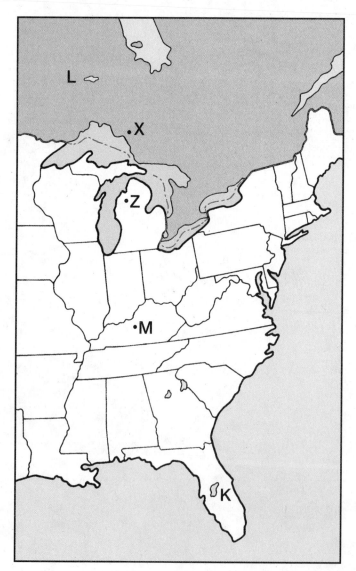

GO TO PART D IN YOUR TEXTBOOK.

Name _____

A

1. The earth makes a circle around the sun one time every ███.
   - hour   - day   - year

2. How many days does it take the earth to make one full circle around the sun?

   _____

3. **Fill in the blanks to show the four seasons.**   winter, _____,

   summer, fall, _____, spring, _____, _____

---

4. Write the missing seasons on the picture below.
5. Shade half of earth A and half of earth C.

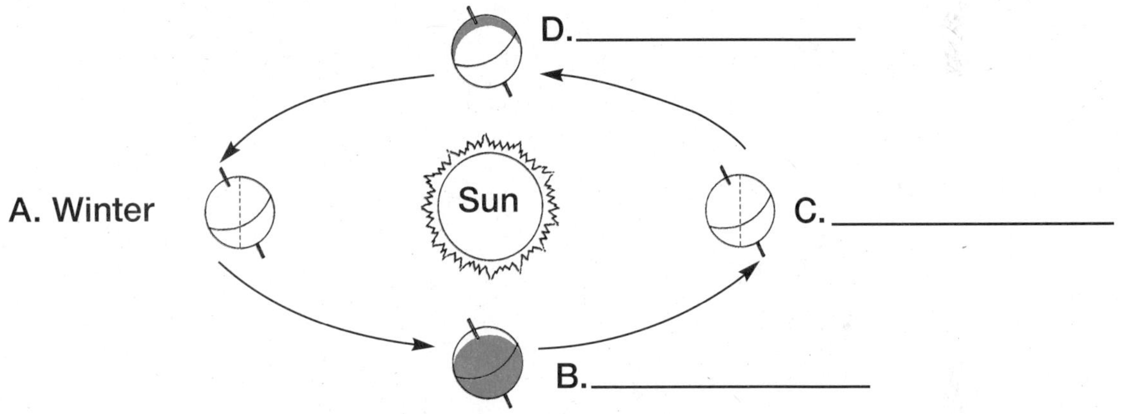

D._____

A. Winter   Sun   C._____

B._____

B   **Story Items**

6. When Tim and Henry were in Kentucky, did Henry want to fly farther

   south? _____

7. Tim said he'd fly with the flock if Henry _____

   _____.

8. Was it **easier** or **harder** to fly with a large flock? _____

9. Were Tim and Henry **near** or **far** from the point of the V? _____

10. Flying near the back of a large flock is like riding your bike ███.
    - with the wind   - against the wind

11. Look at the picture. Write **H** on the goose that has to work the hardest.

12. Color the air that is moving in the same direction the flock is moving.

Review Items

Look at the picture.

13. Shade the part of the earth where it is nighttime.

14. Which side of the earth is closer to the sun, A or B? _____

15. Which side of the earth is in nighttime? _____

16. Which side of the earth is in daytime? _____

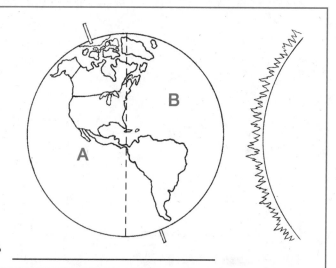

17. How many Great Lakes are there?

_____

18. Color the Great Lakes on the map.

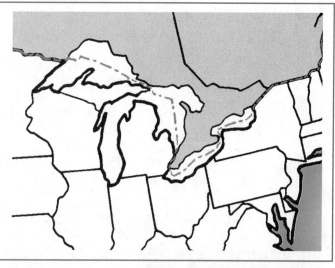

GO TO PART D IN YOUR TEXTBOOK.

Name _____

A

1. Write the number of the earth that has the North Pole tilting away from the sun. _____

2. Write the number of the earth that has the North Pole tilting toward the sun.

   _____

3. Write the number of the earth that has darkness all around the North Pole.

   _____

4. Write the number of the earth that has daylight all around the North Pole.

   _____

Write which season each earth in the picture shows.

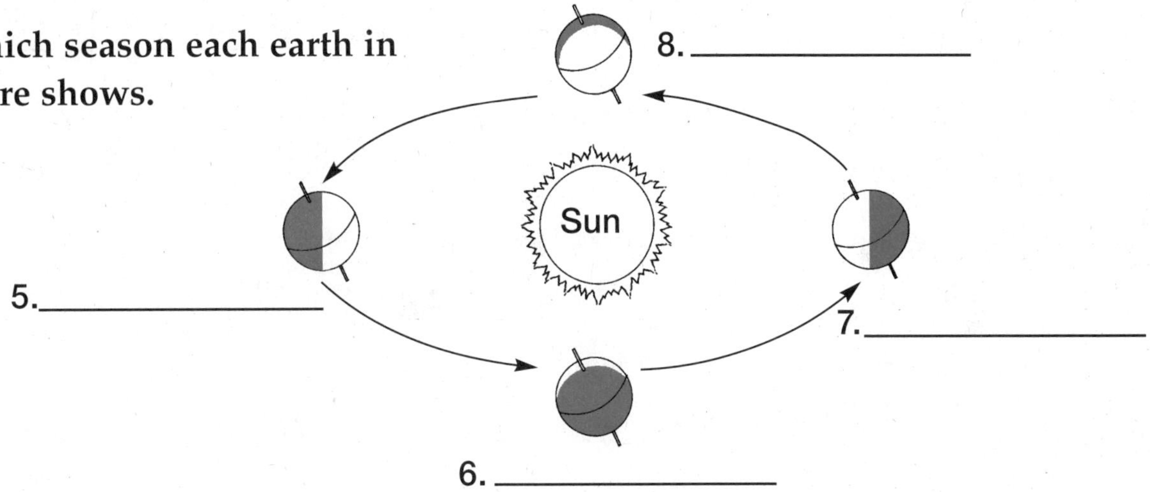

8. _____

5. _____

7. _____

6. _____

9. The picture shows the sun and two balls. **Fix up the balls so that half of each ball is in sunlight and half is in shadow.**

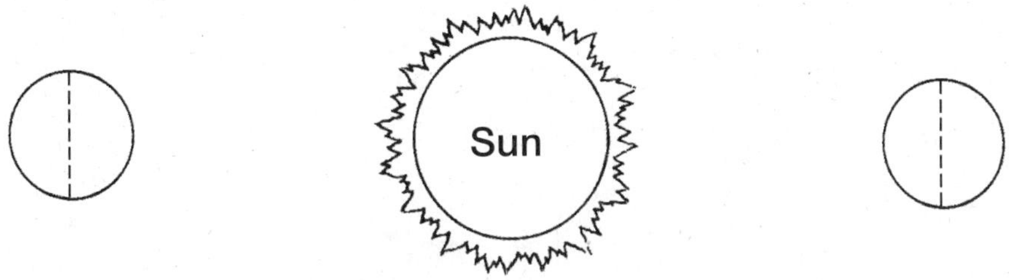

10. During winter at the North Pole, how often does the sun shine?
    • never   • all the time

11. During summer at the North Pole, how often does the sun shine?

    • never   • all the time

12. What season is it at the North Pole when the North Pole tilts **toward** the sun? _____

13. What season is it at the North Pole when the North Pole tilts **away from** the sun? _____

B   **Story Items**

14. The flock started out at Jackson Lake in the state of _____.

15. The flock landed at Newmans Lake in the state of _____.

16. The flock rested for _____ days.

17. Then the flock flew to _____ Lake in the state of _____.

18. The flock they were flying with went on to _____ Lake.

19. **Underline** the geese Tim was looking forward to seeing.

    • children   • friends   • dad   • grandchildren   • mom

20. **Underline** the geese Henry was looking forward to seeing.

    • children   • friends   • dad   • grandchildren   • mom

21. What was Henry going to miss? _____

Review Items

22. Write **H** on the goose in the picture that has to work the hardest.

23. Color the air that is moving in the same direction the flock is moving.

GO TO PART D IN YOUR TEXTBOOK.

Name _____

A

1. Which letter on the map shows Alaska? _____

2. Which letter shows Canada? _____

3. Which letter shows the main part of the United States? _____

4. Which 2 letters show where Eskimos live? _____ and _____

5. How warm is it during winter in Alaska? _____

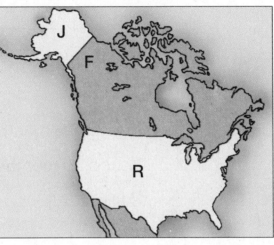

Look at the picture below. **Write the name of each of these objects in the correct place:**

- Eskimo
- sled dogs
- fishing pole
- fishing spear
- sled
- kayak

11. _____

6. _____

10. _____

7. _____

8. _____

9. _____

12. What kind of boat do Eskimos use in the summer? _____

13. Why don't they use those boats in the winter? _____

_____

14. Who met Tim at Crooked Lake? _____

15. Why were they surprised to see Tim? _____

16. The first geese to greet Henry were his _____.

17. Were Henry's children, grandchildren and great grandchildren in the same

    flock as Henry? _____

18. In the winter, Henry gave the young geese practice in flying in a _____.

19. The flocks started to fly north again in the month of _____.

20. They did not arrive at Big Trout Lake until the month of _____.

21. So it took them _____ months to make the trip north.

22. After the flocks arrived at Big Trout Lake, _____ and the other
    young geese left the flock.

23. How old were all these geese? _____

24. Where did those geese move to? _____

25. What lake would this flock go to in the fall? _____

Review Item

26. The picture shows the sun and two balls. **Fix up the balls** so that half of
    each ball is in sunlight and half is in shadow.

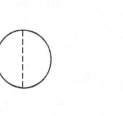 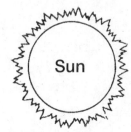

Sun

■■■ GO TO PART D IN YOUR TEXTBOOK. ■■■

22   _Lesson 12_

Name _____

A

Label each animal in the picture below.

2. _____

1. _____

3. _____

4. _____

5. _____

6. _____

7. Which animal in the picture is the biggest? _____

8. Which animal in the picture is the smallest? _____

B

Write these words in the correct places on the map.

  9. pebbled beach   11. summer home   13. ice floe   15. walruses

10. killer whales   12. path   14. seals

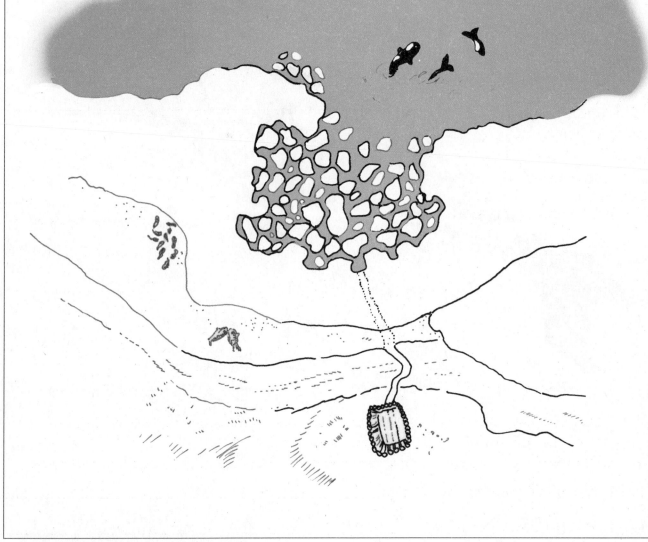

16. At the end of summer, the beach where Oomoo lived was different from the picture in 3 ways. What was different about the ice floe?

    _____

17. What was missing from the water? _____

18. What was missing from the beach? _____

■■■ **GO TO PART E IN YOUR TEXTBOOK.** ■■■

Name _____

A

1. In what season are animals most dangerous in Alaska? _____

2. During what season do female animals in Alaska have babies? _____

3. Female animals fight in the spring to protect _____.

4. Name 2 kinds of Alaskan animals that are dangerous in the spring.

   _____

B **Story Items**

5. What had happened to Usk's mother? _____

6. When Oomoo first saw Usk, Usk was no bigger than a _____.

7. About how tall was Usk when he stood up now? _____

8. Oomoo's father said, "Full-grown bears are not ████."
   - cubs   - pets   - dogs

9. Usk had become less playful last _____.

10. Oomoo didn't run up and hug Usk because she remembered what

    _____ had told her.

11. What did Oolak throw at Usk? _____

12. Why did Oolak do that? _____

Skill Items

Scientists do not ignore ordinary things.

13. What word means that you don't pay attention to something? _____

14. What word tells about things that you see all the time? _____

15. What do we call highly-trained people who study different things about the

    world? _____

Review Items

Write these words in the correct places on the map.

16. ice floe
17. summer home
18. killer whales
19. walruses
20. pebbled beach
21. path
22. seals

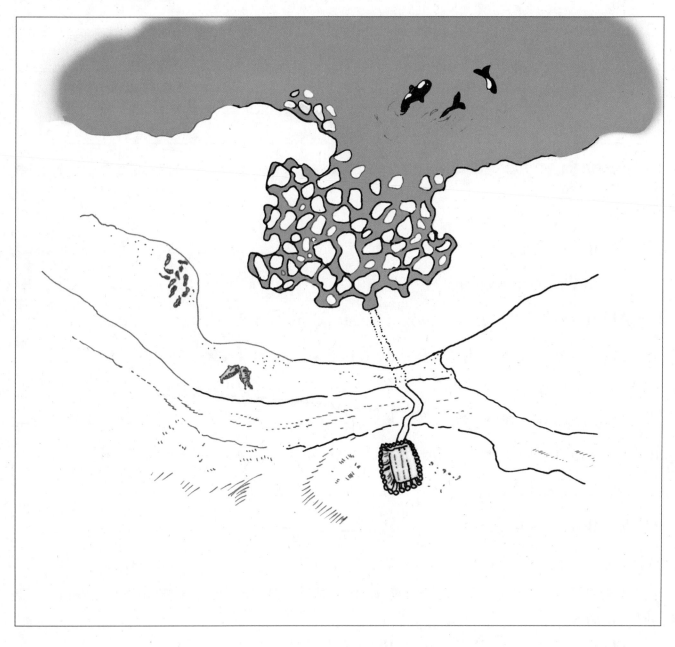

GO TO PART D IN YOUR TEXTBOOK.

26   *Lesson 14*

Name _____

A

1. What state is at the north end of the route on the map?

    _____

2. What country is at the south end of the route? _____

3. About how many miles is the route? _____

4. Write **OO** where Oomoo and Oolak lived.

5. Write **OH** where Old Henry lived in the summertime.

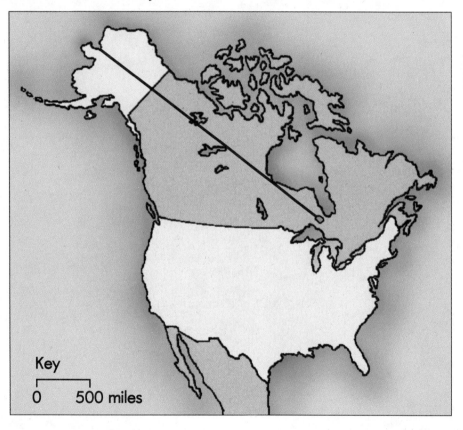

Key

0   500 miles

B   **Story Items**

6. What happened when Usk nudged Oolak with his nose?

    _____

7. Usk started chasing Oomoo after _____

_____ .

8. When Usk caught up to Oomoo, what did he grab?

• boot   • collar

9. Then what did Usk do to Oomoo? _____

10. Who made the children stop playing? _____

11. When Oomoo reached her father, she didn't look at him. Why?

_____

12. Will the father let the children play with Usk? _____

Review Items

13. Write the missing seasons on the picture below.

14. Shade half of earth A and half of earth C.

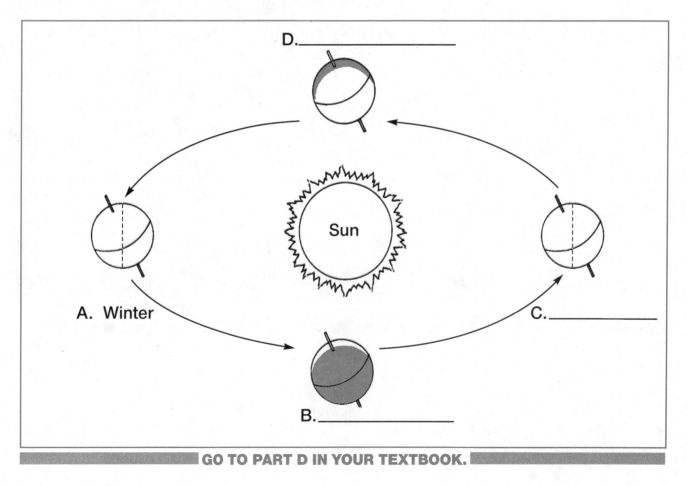

Name _____

A

1. About how long are killer whales? _____

2. Compare the size of killer whales with the size of other whales. **Killer whales** _____ .

3. Are killer whales fish? _____

4. Are killer whales **warm-blooded** or **cold-blooded?** _____

5. Name 3 animals that are warm-blooded. _____

6. Name 3 animals that are cold-blooded. _____

B **Story Items**

7. How long did Oomoo and Oolak have to stay near the summer house?

_____

8. What kind of house was the summer house? _____

9. What kind of house was the winter house? _____

10. Which house was bigger? _____

11. What was the only problem with the summer house? _____

12. Name 3 kinds of biting insects that Alaska has in the spring.

_____

13. Why was Oomoo's summer home in a place where the wind blew hard?

_____

14. What were the male seals on the beach fighting for?

_____

15. What were the killer whales waiting for?

_____

16. What were Oomoo and her father in when the killer whales came close to

them? _____

17. How many whales were there? _____

Skill Items

Here are three events that happened in the story:
   a. They were swarming by the thousands on the beach about half a mile from
      Oomoo's summer home.
   b. Then Oomoo's father ordered Oomoo to stay near their summer house for
      two full days.
   c. "I never want to be that close to killer whales again," she said to herself.

18. Write the letter of the event that happened near the beginning of the story. ____

19. Write the letter of the event that happened near the middle of the story. _____

20. Write the letter of the event that happened near the end of the story. _____

Review Items

21. How many Great Lakes are there? _____

22. Color the
    Great Lakes
    on the map.

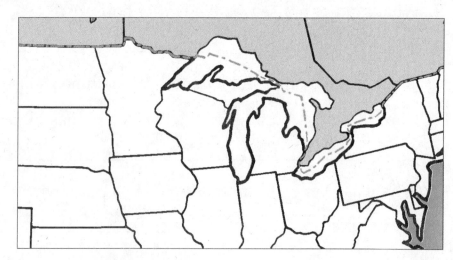

23. **Fill in the blanks to show the four seasons.**
    winter, _____, summer, fall, _____, spring,

    _____, _____.

GO TO PART D IN YOUR TEXTBOOK.

30   *Lesson 16*

Name _____

A

Here are three events that happened in the story:

  a. During the winter, you can walk far out on the frozen ocean.

  b. But even if the killer whales didn't attack you, you would die within a few minutes after you went into the water.

  c. For a moment, Oomoo was going to say, "That's a pretty long way to drift."

1. Write the letter of the event that happened near the beginning of the story. ____

2. Write the letter of the event that happened near the middle of the story. ____

3. Write the letter of the event that happened near the end of the story. _____

B   Story Items

4. During which season do ice floes start? _____

5. During the winter in Alaska, you can walk far out on the ocean. Tell why.

  _____

6. Do ice floes make noise in the winter? _____

7. Why do ice floes make noise in the spring? _____

  _____

8. When Oomoo played on the ice floe in the spring, she could never go out to the end of the ice floe. What was at the end of the ice floe? _____

9. You are out in the ocean on an ice chunk that melts. Name 2 ways you could die. _____

  _____

10. Oomoo and Oolak were drifting on something. What was it? _____

11. Write **north, south, east** and **west** in the boxes.

12. Make an **X** where the killer whales stay.

13. Make a **Y** on an ice chunk where Oomoo is not supposed to go.

14. Make a **Z** on the ice chunk Oomoo and Oolak are on.

15. **Make an arrow** from the **Z** to where they would go if the wind blows from the east. Show the path the ice chunk should follow.

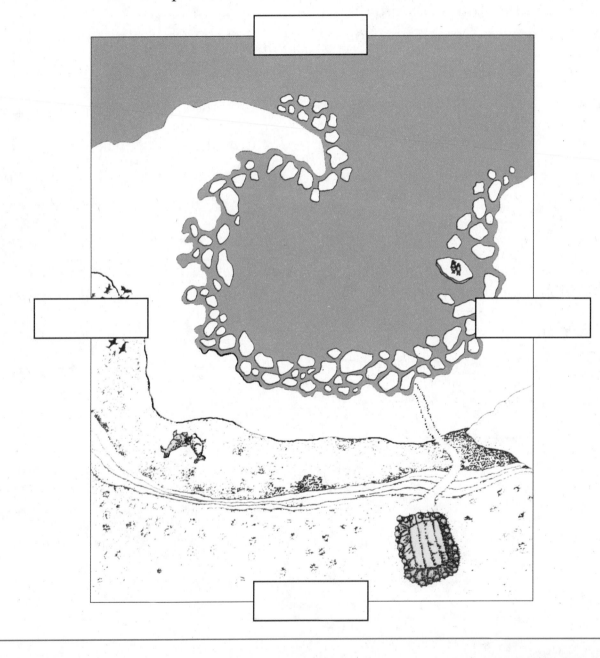

GO TO PART C IN YOUR TEXTBOOK.

Name _____

A

1. Name 2 things that can make an ice chunk drift. _____

2. In which direction will you drift when you're in an ocean current?

   _____

3. In which direction will you drift when you're in a strong wind?

   _____

4. Write **north, south, east** and **west** in the correct boxes.

5. In which direction is ocean current **A** moving? _____

6. In which direction is ocean current **B** moving? _____

7. Which direction is the wind coming from? _____

8. Make an arrow **above** ice chunk **C** to show the direction the current will move the ice chunk.

9. Make an arrow **above** ice chunk **D** to show the direction the current will move the ice chunk.

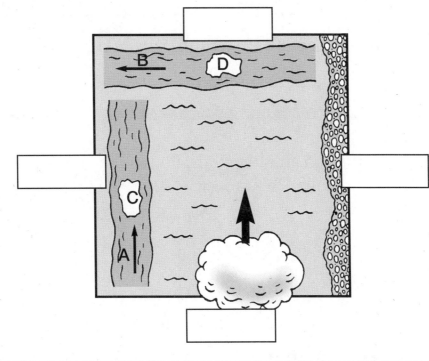

B Story Items

10. If you're out on the ocean and you spot a green cloud, what should you do?

_____

11. What 2 things do those clouds bring? _____

12. Did Oomoo and Oolak follow the rule about watching the sky? _____

13. Was the water **smooth** or **rough** where the wind hit the water? _____

14. How fast was the wind moving? _____

15. In which direction was the ice chunk headed? _____

16. Name the direction the ice chunk was drifting **before** the big wind came up.

_____

17. Name the direction the ice chunk was drifting **after** the big wind hit it.

_____

18. Where were the flies and mosquitoes thick?
    - near the shore
    - near the tent
    - over the ocean

19. Where were the flies and mosquitoes not as thick?
    - near the shore
    - near the tent
    - over the ocean

20. What did Oomoo and Oolak do to make the ice chunk rock?

_____

21. Name 2 things that tell about the cloud that Oomoo saw.

_____

Review Items

22. The picture shows the sun and two balls. Fix up the balls so that half of each ball is in sunlight and half is in shadow.

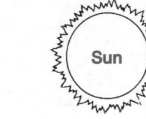

GO TO PART D IN YOUR TEXTBOOK.

Name _____

Story Items

1. The wind blew Oomoo and Oolak off course. In which direction were they drifting before the big wind blew?

   _____

2. In which direction did the big wind blow them? _____

3. When Oomoo heard Oolak's voice, she turned to look at him. Where was

   Oolak? _____

4. What did Oomoo put in the water to help Oolak? _____

5. Just as Oomoo was sliding off the ice chunk, a huge wave hit it. Where did

   Oomoo and Oolak end up? _____

6. When Oolak asked Oomoo, "Are we going to die?" did Oomoo say what

   she really thought? _____

7. When the wind died down, rain and hail began to fall. Which made more

   noise, the **wind** or the **rain and hail**?_____

8. Which was colder, the **ocean water** or the **rain**? _____

9. How long did the rain come down hard?

   - 10 minutes   • an hour   • half an hour

10. At the end of the story, what did Oomoo see beyond the ice floe?

    _____

11. Did she tell Oolak what she saw? _____

12. Tell why. _____

13. After the big wind died down, Oomoo and Oolak shouted for help. Why

    couldn't anyone hear them? _____

14. Make an arrow from the **X** to the C-shaped ice floe. Show the path the ice chunk was supposed to follow.

15. Which letter shows where the ice chunk was at the end of today's story? _____

16. Which letter shows where the killer whales were? _____

17. Make an arrow from the **Q** to show which way the big wind blew.

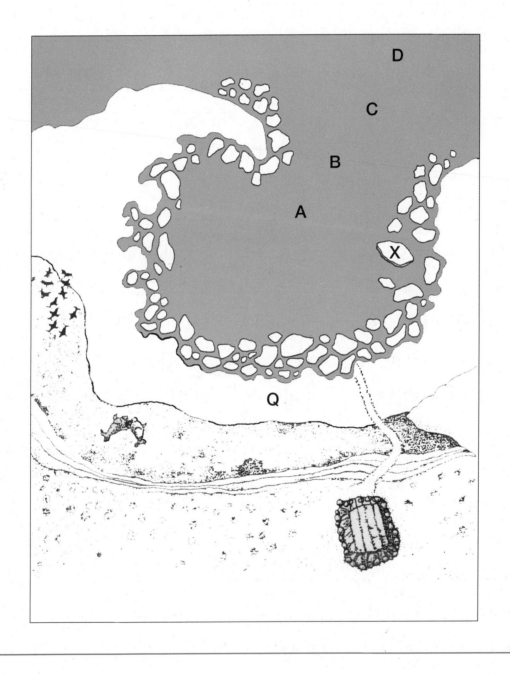

GO TO PART C IN YOUR TEXTBOOK.

Name _____

A

1. What are clouds made of? _____

2. What kind of cloud does picture **A** show? _____

3. Write the letter of the clouds that may stay in the sky for days at a time. _____

4. Write the letter of the storm clouds. _____

5. Write the letter of the clouds that have frozen drops of water. _____

6. Write the letter of the clouds that may be five miles high. _____

7. Look at cloud A. At which number does a drop of water start? _____

8. What happens to the drop at the number **2**? _____

9. Draw 2 arrows on cloud **A** to show how a hailstone forms and returns to 1.

A

B

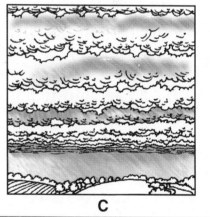
C

10. If you break a hailstone in half, what will you see inside the hailstone?

_____

11. The picture shows half of a hailstone. How many times did the stone

go through a cloud? _____

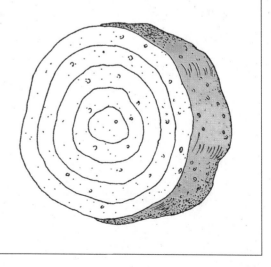

B Story Items

12. Oomoo slapped her boot on the ice to make noise. Why did she want the people on shore to hear the noise? _____

_____

13. Why did she want the killer whales to hear the noise? _____

_____

14. Was Oomoo sure that someone would hear her? _____

15. About how far was the ice chunk from the tent? _____

16. About how far was the ice chunk from the killer whales? _____

Review Items

17. Write **north, south, east** and **west** in the correct boxes.

18. In which direction is ocean current **J** moving? _____

19. In which direction is ocean current **K** moving? _____

20. Which direction is the wind coming from? _____

21. Make an arrow above ice chunk **L** to show the direction the current will move the ice chunk.

22. Make an arrow above ice chunk **M** to show the direction the current will move the ice chunk.

GO TO PART D IN YOUR TEXTBOOK.

Name _____

A

Look at the pile in the picture.

1. Things closer to the bottom of the pile went into the pile _____.

2. Which object went into the pile **first**?
_____

3. Which object went into the pile **last**?
_____

4. Which object went into the pile **earlier**—the knife or the book?
_____

5. Which object went into the pile **earlier**—the pencil or the cup?
_____

6. Which object went into the pile **just after** the bone? _____

7. Which object went into the pile **just after** the pencil? _____

B Story Items

8. Oomoo and Oolak dug their heels into dents in the ice so that Usk could not _____.

9. What did Oomoo see that scared her? _____

10. Why did Oomoo slap the ice with her hand?

    _____

11. While Oomoo and Oolak sat by the tent, they had to study

    _____ and _____.

12. They had to do that so they would remember to look _____.

13. Did Oomoo find out why the killer whale didn't attack Usk? _____

14. The people of the village formed a big ring. Who stood in the middle of the

    ring? _____

15. What did the women give Usk? _____

16. What did Oomoo's father paint on each side of Usk? _____

17. Why were Oomoo and Oolak so proud of Usk?

    _____

Review Items

18. **Fill in the blanks to show the four seasons.**

    winter, _____, summer, fall, _____,

    spring, _____, _____

GO TO PART D IN YOUR TEXTBOOK.

Name _____

Story Items

1. Write the letter of the layer that
   went into the pile **first**. _____

2. Write the letter of the layer that
   went into the pile **next**. _____

3. Write the letter of the layer that
   went into the pile **last**. _____

4. Which layer went into the pile
   earlier—B or C? _____

5. Which layer went into the pile
   earlier—A or C? _____

6. Write the letter of the layer
   where we would find the
   skeletons of humans. _____

7. Write the letter of the layer that
   has dinosaur skeletons. _____

8. Write the letter of the layer
   where we find the skeletons of
   horses. _____

9. What's the name of layer C? _____

10. Write the letter of the layer we live in. _____

11. Are there any dinosaur skeletons in layer D? _____

12. Which came earlier on Earth, dinosaurs or horses? _____

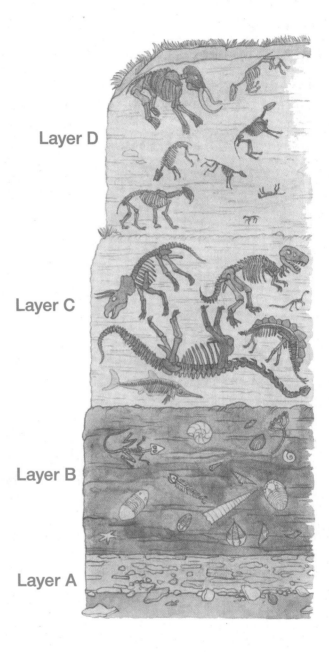

Layer D

Layer C

Layer B

Layer A

13. Which came earlier on Earth, strange sea animals or dinosaurs? _____

14. What kind of animals lived in the Mesozoic? _____

Review Items

15. Write the missing seasons on the picture below.

16. Shade half of Earth **A** and half of Earth **C**.

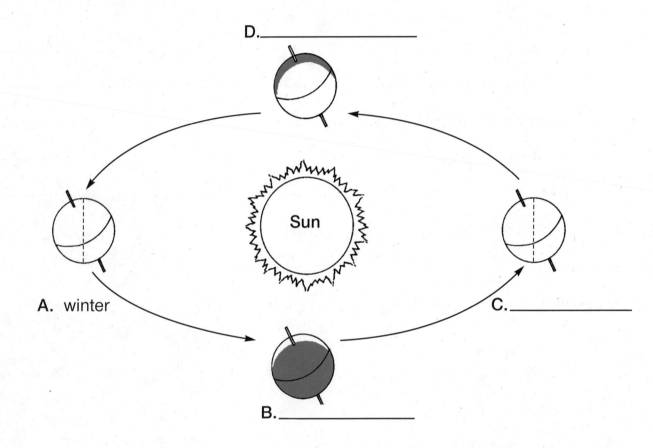

D._____

Sun

A. winter

C._____

B._____

GO TO PART C IN YOUR TEXTBOOK.

Name _____

A **Story Items**

1. How old was Edna Parker? _____

2. How did Edna usually feel on the ship?

  • happy   • bored   • nervous

3. Why wouldn't Edna be bored on this trip? _____

_____

4. Where was the ship starting from? _____

5. Where was it going? _____

6. How far was the trip? _____

7. How long would it take?

  • more than one day   • one day   • less than one day

8. Draw an **arrow** on the map below to show the trip.

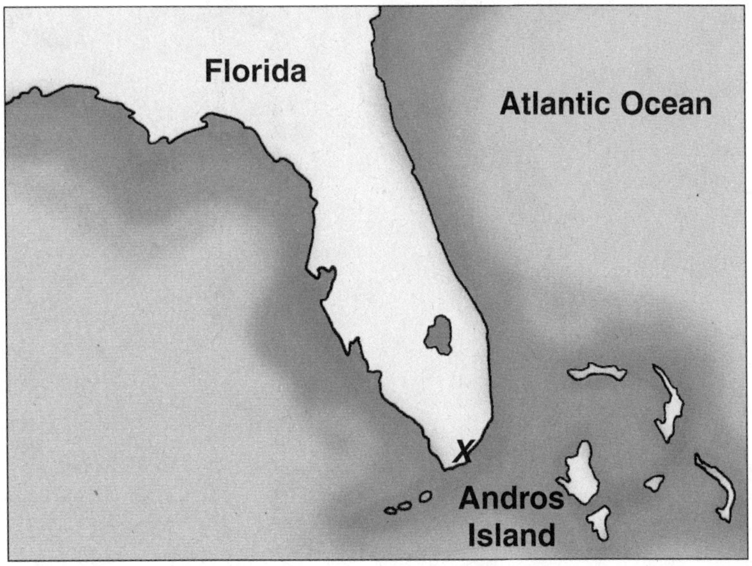

Florida

Atlantic Ocean

Andros Island

9. The ship would pass through a place where hundreds of ships have sunk or been lost. Name that place. _____

10. **Underline** the 3 things you find in the Bermuda Triangle.
    - huge waves
    - whirlpools
    - mountains
    - sudden storms
    - streams
    - icebergs

11. As the girls left the map room, Captain Parker told them to stay away from the sides of the ship and the _____.

Review Items

Look at the picture below.

12. Shade the part of the earth where it is nighttime.

13. Which side of the earth is closer to the sun, **A** or **B**? _____

14. Which side of the earth is in nighttime? _____

15. Which side of the earth is in daytime? _____

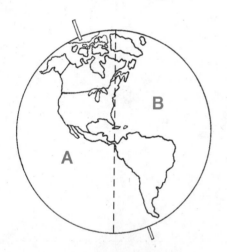
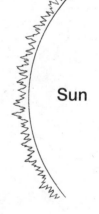

GO TO PART D IN YOUR TEXTBOOK.

44   *Lesson 24*

Name _____

A Story Items

1. How old was Edna Parker? _____

2. How did Edna usually feel on the ship?

      • happy   • bored   • nervous

3. As the girls left the map room, Captain Parker told them to stay away from

   the _____ and the _____.

4. Why didn't the girls stay in the galley?

   • The cook complained about his tooth.
   • It was dirty.
   • It smelled bad.

5. The girls didn't stay in the engine room because the engineer told them that
   they would have to ▬▬▬.

      • go to the galley   • work   • sing

6. The girls decided not to climb the ▬▬▬.

      • stairs   • mast   • flag pole

7. Did any of the crew members play with Edna and Carla? _____

8. Carla wanted to pretend that they were ▬▬▬.

      • on an island   • on their own ship
           • on top of a mountain

9. Which girl wanted to play in the lifeboat? _____

10. How many crew members were watching while Edna and Carla talked

    about playing in the lifeboat? _____

Story Items

After Edna and Carla left the map room, they went to different places on the ship.

11. Write the letter that shows where they went just after they left the map room. _____

12. Write the letter that shows where they went next. _____

13. Write the letter that shows where they sat down in the sun. _____

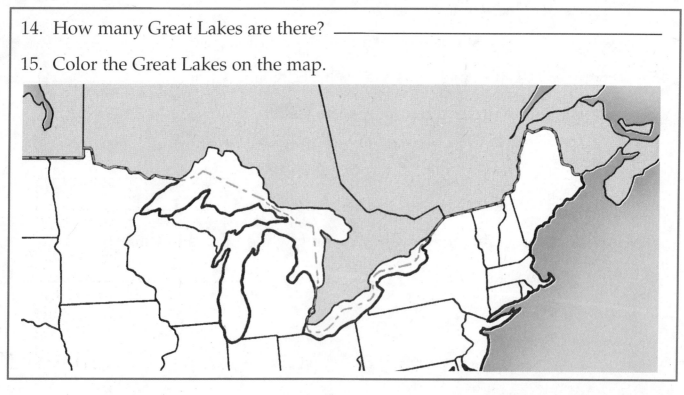

Review Items

14. How many Great Lakes are there? _____

15. Color the Great Lakes on the map.

GO TO PART C IN YOUR TEXTBOOK.

Name _____

A **Story Items**

1. When today's story began, Edna and Carla were pretending they had their

    own ship. Who was the captain? _____

2. **Underline** 3 things the first mate did to look more like a sailor.
    - took off her shoes
    - wore short pants
    - wore a sailor suit
    - rolled up her pants
    - wrapped a handkerchief around her head

3. What happened to the lifeboat when the girls were in it?

    - It dropped into the water.
    - It turned over.
    - It rang a bell.

4. What part of the lifeboat hit the water first, the bow or the stern? _____

5. What happened to Edna when the boat hit the water?

    - She fell out of the boat.
    - She bumped into Carla.
    - She hit her head.

6. What 2 things did the girls do to make the people on the large ship notice

    them? _____

    _____

7. Did anyone notice them? _____

8. When Edna and Carla turned around, they saw one of these clouds. Write

    the letter of that cloud. _____

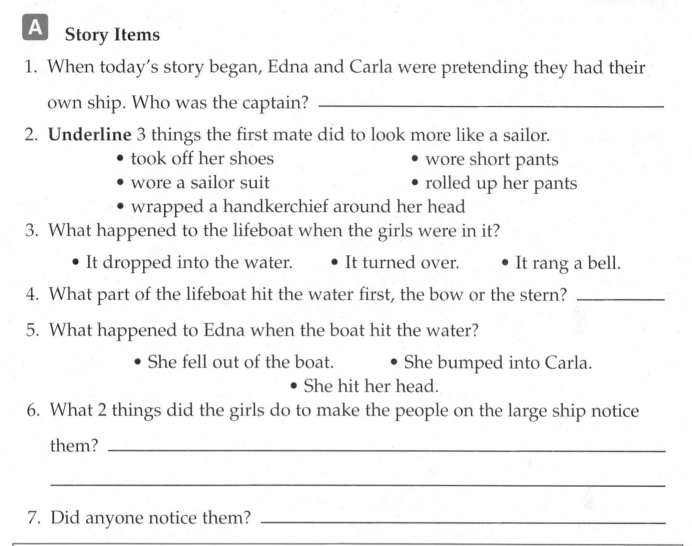

A   B   C

9. When the girls started bailing, there was about _____ inches of water in the boat.

10. What made the girls stop bailing?

    • a whirlpool   • a wind   • an airplane

11. At the end of the story, how high were the waves? _____

12. How fast were the winds moving? _____

Review Items

13. In which direction do geese migrate in the fall? _____

14. In which direction do geese migrate in the spring? _____

15. Write the directions **north, south, east** and **west** in the boxes.

16. Make a line that starts at the circle on the map and goes north.

17. If you start at the circle and move to the number **2,** in which direction do you go? _____

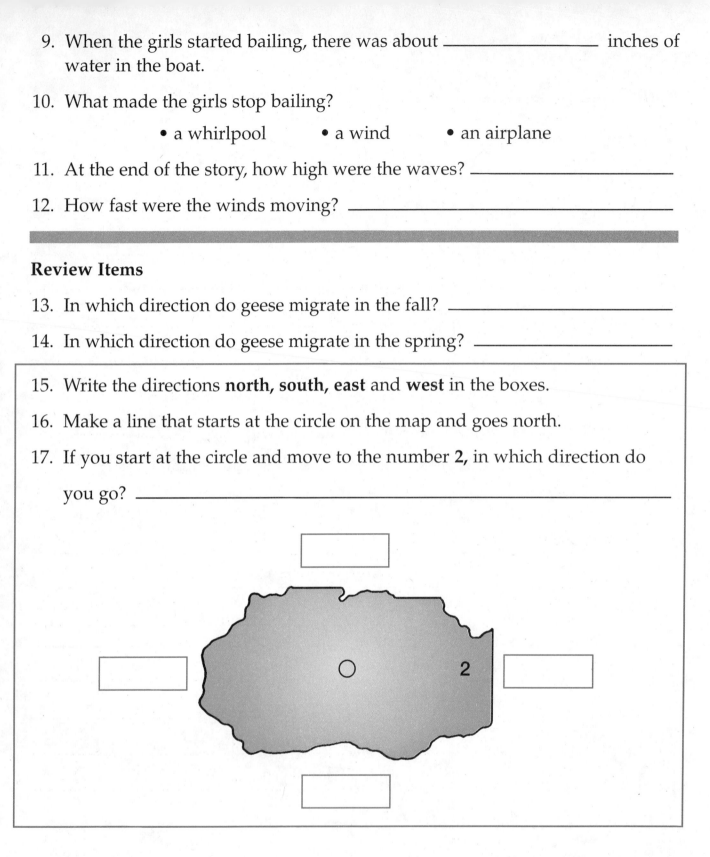

GO TO PART C IN YOUR TEXTBOOK.

Name _____

A

1. Whirlpools are made up of moving _____.

2. A whirlpool is shaped like a _____.

3. What happens to something that gets caught in a whirlpool? _____

_____

4. What happened to the lifeboat when the girls got in it? _____

_____

5. When today's story began, Carla shouted that she saw land. What did she really see? _____

6. When could Edna see in the distance?

   • at the top of a wave   • at the bottom of a wave

7. After the giant wave hit, the boat was being sucked into a

_____.

8. Some things happened so fast that Carla and Edna had to try to figure out what they were. What two things did Edna remember? _____

_____.

9. What made the blinding flash? _____

10. What fell from the sky? _____

11. Did the boat land near the whirlpool? _____

12. How did Edna feel when the sea was calm again? _____

13. About how deep was the water when Edna stepped out of the lifeboat?

_____

14. About how far was it from the lifeboat to the beach? _____

Review Items

15. Write **north**, **south**, **east** and **west** in the correct boxes.

16. In which direction is ocean current **P** moving? _____

17. In which direction is ocean current **Q** moving? _____

18. Which direction is the wind coming from? _____

19. Make an arrow next to ice chunk **R** to show the direction the current will move the ice chunk.

20. Make an arrow above ice chunk **S** to show the direction the current will move the ice chunk.

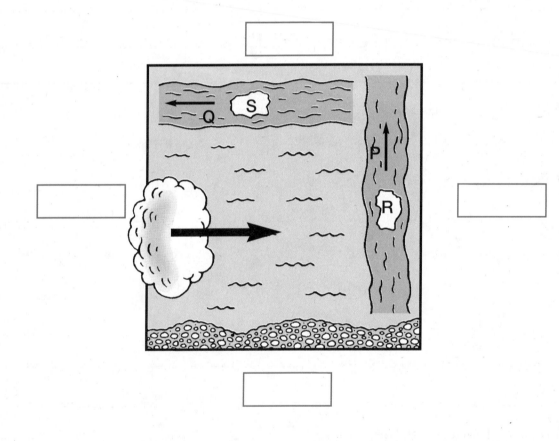

GO TO PART D IN YOUR TEXTBOOK.

Name _____

A Story Items

1. After the giant wave hit the boat in the last story, what was the boat being

   sucked into? _____

2. Some things happened so fast that Carla and Edna had to try to figure out

   what they were. What made the blinding flash? _____

3. What fell from the sky? _____

4. About how far was it from the lifeboat to the beach? _____

5. What was right behind the beach? _____

6. What was strange about the sand on the beach? _____

7. Edna and Carla woke up when it was dark. What woke them up?

   _____

8. The animal Edna saw was as big as some of the _____.

9. Did the animal walk on **4 legs** or **2 legs?** _____

10. Where did the girls go to spend the last part of the night?

    _____

11. Did the girls get much sleep? _____

12. What was the first thing the girls discovered in the red sand?

    _____

13. The footprints were ▉▉▉ long.
    - a foot   • a yard   • half a meter

Review Items

14. Write the letter of the earth that shows the person in daytime.

    _____

15. Write the letter of the earth that shows the person 6 hours later.

    _____

16. Write the letter that shows the person another 6 hours later.

    _____

17. Write the letter that shows the person another 6 hours later.

    _____

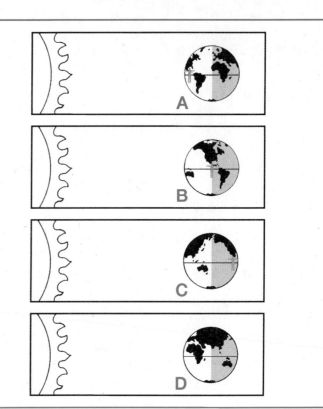

18. Which letter on the map shows Alaska? _____

19. Which letter shows Canada?

    _____

20. Which letter shows the main part of the United States? _____

21. Which 2 letters show where Eskimos live? _____

22. How warm is it during winter in Alaska? _____

GO TO PART C IN YOUR TEXTBOOK.

Name _____

A   Story Items

1. What was strange about the sand on the beach where Edna and Carla

   landed? _____

2. The footprints of the animal were _____ long.

3. How many toes did each footprint have? _____

4. What did the size of the footprints tell about the size of the animal?
   - It was bigger than a bear.
   - It was a bear.
   - It was smaller than a bear.

5. How did Edna know that the animal was very heavy?
   - The footprints were long.
   - The footprints made deep dents.
   - The footprints had 3 toes.

6. What part of the animal made the deep groove between the footprints?

   _____

7. Edna wasn't sure if she wanted to follow the animal. **Underline** 2 things that
   tell what the parts of her mind wanted to do.
   - read about dinosaurs
   - run
   - think
   - learn more about the animal
   - find something to eat

8. Edna saw something next to the path that she recognized from a picture in a
   book. What did she see?
   - a stream
   - a tree
   - a bug

9. What else was in that picture?
   - dinosaurs
   - ships
   - rocks

10. How did that make her feel? _____

11. Write the letter of the footprint made by the heaviest animal. _____

12. Write the letter of the footprint made by the lightest animal. _____

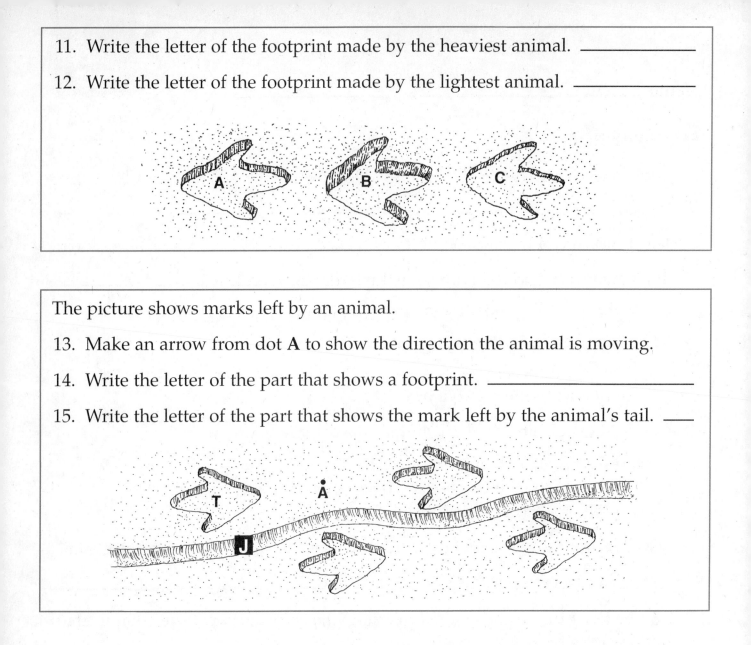

The picture shows marks left by an animal.

13. Make an arrow from dot **A** to show the direction the animal is moving.

14. Write the letter of the part that shows a footprint. _____

15. Write the letter of the part that shows the mark left by the animal's tail. ____

GO TO PART C IN YOUR TEXTBOOK.

Name _____

A Story Items

1. Edna and Carla saw a winged animal. Was that animal a bird? _____

2. How do you know?

   • It had teeth.   • It didn't have a beak.   • It didn't have feathers.

3. Its wings were covered with something that looked like ▉▉▉.

   • feathers   • leather   • hair

4. How long ago did those winged animals live on Earth?

   • a thousand years ago
   • a million years ago
   • a hundred million years ago

5. **Underline** the name of the dinosaur the girls saw.

   • Triceratops   • Mammoth   • Tyrannosaurus

6. What cracked the tree that Edna was hiding behind?

   • Tyrannosaurus's head   • Tyrannosaurus's foot   • Tyrannosaurus's tail

7. What happened to Edna when the tree cracked? _____

8. Before Edna started to run, she heard noises from the clearing. What made the leathery flapping sound?

   • Tyrannosaurus   • the flying dinosaur   • Carla

9. Whose bones were making the crunching sound? _____

10. Tyrannosaurus didn't hear Edna running because it was ▉▉▉.

    • sleeping   • eating   • scratching

11. As Edna ran through the jungle toward the beach, what did she see on the path? _____

12. Did Edna slow down when she saw it? _____

13. When Edna got to the beach, she realized that something was wrong. What was wrong? _____

Review Items

14. Write **north, south, east** and **west** in the correct boxes.

15. In which direction is ocean current **F** moving? _____

16. In which direction is ocean current **G** moving? _____

17. Which direction is the wind coming from? _____

18. Make an arrow above ice chunk **H** to show the direction the current will move the ice chunk.

19. Make an arrow above ice chunk **I** to show the direction the current will move the ice chunk.

Name _____

A Story Items

1. At the beginning of the story, Edna was trying to decide something. **Underline** what she was trying to decide.

   - whether she should go back into the jungle
   - whether she should hide under the boat
   - whether she should call for help

2. Edna didn't call to Carla because the sound would ▮▮▮▮ .

   - make the birds fly
   - not be loud enough
   - catch the dinosaur's attention

3. When Edna was near the clearing, she couldn't see Tyrannosaurus. **Underline 2** ways she knew that Tyrannosaurus was nearby.

   - She could feel its skin.
   - She could hear it.
   - She could smell it.
   - She could taste it.

4. Carla was lying very still because ▮▮▮▮ .

   - Tyrannosaurus was near
   - the leaves were wet
   - Edna was watching

5. Carla didn't get up because her leg was _____ .

6. Edna made up a plan to save Carla. How was Edna going to catch Tyrannosaurus's attention? _____

   _____

7. In Edna's plan, what would Tyrannosaurus do? _____

   _____

8. What would Carla do? _____

_____

9. Did Edna get to try her plan? _____

10. What came into the clearing when Tyrannosaurus was moving back and

forth? _____

11. What were Edna and Carla trying to do at the end of the story?

_____

Review Items

12. What kind of boat do Eskimos use in the summer? _____

13. Why don't they use those boats in the winter? _____

_____

14. During which season do ice floes start? _____

15. During winter in Alaska, you can walk far out on the ocean. Tell why.

_____

16. Do ice floes make noise in the winter? _____

17. Why do ice floes make noise in the spring? _____

_____

GO TO PART C IN YOUR TEXTBOOK.

58   *Lesson 32*

Name _____

A

1. What comes out of a volcano? _____

2. Draw arrows at **A,** at **B** and at **C** to show the way the melted rock moves.

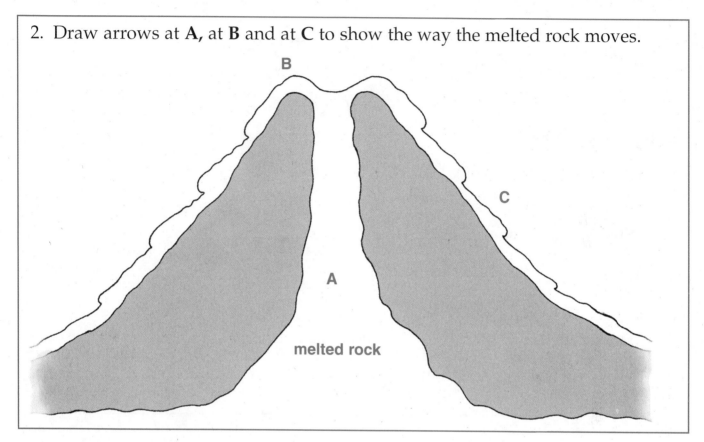

melted rock

3. Two things happen to melted rock when it moves down the sides of a volcano. **Underline** those 2 things.

- It gets hotter.
- It gets cooler.
- It hardens.
- It runs faster.
- It gets softer.

4. What is it called when the earth shakes and cracks? _____

B Story Items

5. When Edna was near the clearing in the last story, she couldn't see Tyrannosaurus. **Underline** 2 ways she knew that Tyrannosaurus was nearby.

   - She could taste it.
   - She could hear it.
   - She could feel its skin.
   - She could smell it.

6. What came into the clearing when Tyrannosaurus was moving back and forth? _____

7. At the beginning of today's story, Tyrannosaurus was fighting ▆▆▆.

   - Triceratops   • a mammoth   • a flying dinosaur

8. Who won the fight? _____

9. What kept making the earth rock from side to side?

   - earthquakes   • the volcano   • the storm

10. What made the boiling cloud of smoke? _____

11. Why did Edna fall down on the beach? _____

_____

12. When the girls were in shallow water, what formed underwater?

_____

13. Who fell into the crack? _____

14. What did the volcano do just after Edna got into the boat?

_____

15. Did the girls know where they were going to go at the end of the story?

_____

GO TO PART D IN YOUR TEXTBOOK.

Name _____

A Story Items

1. What color was the water where it was shallow? _____

2. What color was the water where it was deepest? _____

3. Edna had blisters on her hands from _____.

4. As the girls sat in the lifeboat, they could see a billowing cloud in the distance. What was making that cloud? _____

5. Name 2 kinds of supplies you'd need to stay on the ocean for a long time.

   _____

6. In which direction were the girls drifting? _____

7. Edna was thirsty. Why didn't she drink some ocean water?

   • It was warm.   • It was salty.   • It was dirty.

8. What made the boat move faster and faster? _____

9. While the lifeboat was in the whirlpool, why did the clouds seem to be spinning?

   • because of the wind   • because the boat was spinning
   • because she was sick

10. Did the girls know how they got out of the whirlpool? _____

11. The water in the bottom of the boat was very warm, so that water had been in the boat for ████.

    • a few seconds   • a few minutes   • a long time

12. After Edna woke up, she saw fish. What color was the water? _____

13. Why was Edna thinking about chewing on raw fish?

    • because she needed toothpaste
    • because she needed food
    • because she needed water

Review Items

14. Draw arrows at **X**, at **Y** and at **Z** to show the way the melted rock moves.

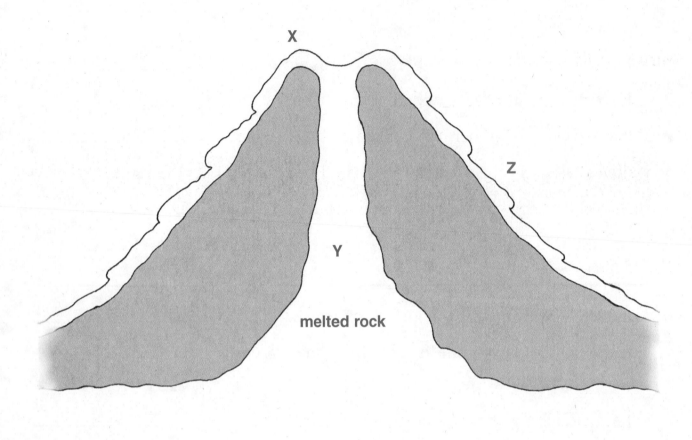

melted rock

GO TO PART D IN YOUR TEXTBOOK.

Name _____

A Story Items

1. What did Edna see that told her a ship was in the distance? _____

2. How did she know it wasn't from the island?
   - It billowed.
   - It didn't billow.
   - It was black.

3. Whose ship was it? _____

4. Why did Edna feel ashamed when she saw her father? _____
   _____

5. The girls needed some care when they got back on the ship. Name 3 things
   they needed. _____
   _____

6. Did Captain Parker believe the girls' story? _____

7. On what day of the week did the girls go overboard? _____

8. On what day of the week did the girls think it was when they got back on
   the ship? _____

9. What day was it really when they got back on the ship? _____

10. What did Edna find to make her think the adventure really happened?
    _____

11. The sand in Edna's pocket must have come from _____ .

Review Items

12. How long ago did dinosaurs live on Earth? _____

13. What is it called when the earth shakes and cracks? _____

14. Write the missing seasons on the picture below.

15. Shade half of earth A and half of earth C.

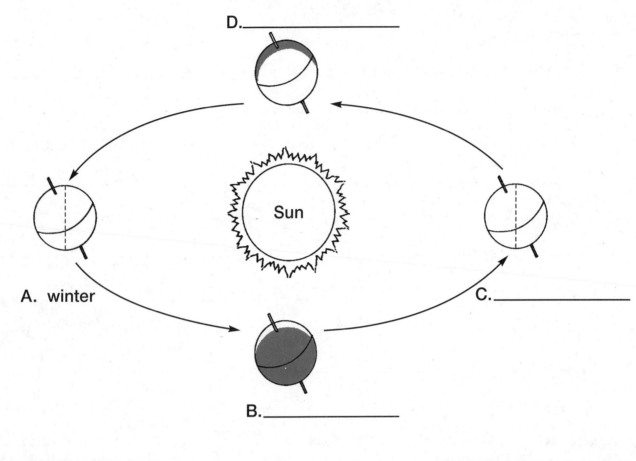

D._____

Sun

A. winter

C._____

B._____

GO TO PART C IN YOUR TEXTBOOK.

Name _____

A

1. Name 3 things that are made by humans. _____

   _____

2. What is a person doing when the person makes an object for the first time?

   _____

3. The person who makes an object for the first time is called an

   _____.

4. The object the person makes is called an _____.

5. Most of the things that we use every day were invented after the year ▓▓▓▓.
   - 1800   - 1900   - 2200

6. **Underline** the 5 things that were not invented by anybody.
   - chairs   - horses   - flowers   - grass   - planes
   - bottles   - snakes   - spiders   - rugs

B   **Story Items**

7. **Underline** 2 reasons it was embarrassing to go places with Grandmother Esther.

   - She walked fast.   - She talked a lot.
   - She chewed gum.   - She mumbled to herself.
   - She talked loudly.

8. What did Grandmother Esther like to talk about?

   _____

9. Did she look at the displays of dinosaurs for a long time? _____

10. **Underline** 3 displays that Grandmother Esther wanted to see.

    - radios   - cave people   - clothing
    - airplanes   - horses   - automobiles

11. Grandmother Esther made a speech in the exhibit hall about the people who invented the airplane. How did Leonard feel?

_____

12. What did the other people in the exhibit hall do after the speech?

_____

Review Items

13. Write the missing seasons on the picture below.
14. Shade half of earth **A** and half of earth **C**.

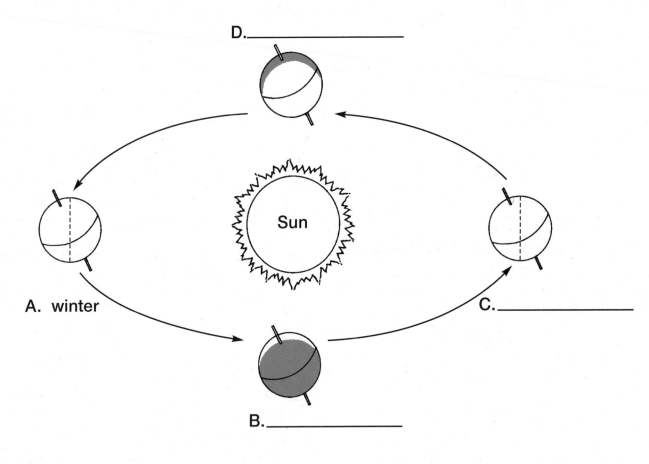

D._____

Sun

A. winter

C._____

B._____

GO TO PART D IN YOUR TEXTBOOK.

Name _____

A **Story Items**

1. What was wrong with the waterbed that Grandmother Esther invented?

   _____

2. What did Grandmother Esther's folding bike sometimes do when a person

   was riding it? _____

3. **Underline** 2 things that Grandmother Esther ate for lunch.

   - apple   - egg   - donut
   - cake   - cookie   - sandwich

4. Did Leonard know what he wanted to invent? _____

5. At first Leonard thought that he couldn't be an inventor because

   _____

   _____.

6. Did Grandmother Esther agree? _____

7. The men who invented the first airplane saw a need. What need?

   _____

8. There was a need for the first automobile because people had problems with horses. **Underline** 2 problems.

   - Horses need care.   - Horses are strong.
   - Horses are slow.   - Horses like to run.

9. The first thing you do when you think like an inventor is find a _____.

10. What's the next thing you do?

   - Ask questions.
   - Meet the need.
   - Go to a museum.

Review Items

11. Draw arrows at **J,** at **K** and at **L** to show the way the melted rock moves.

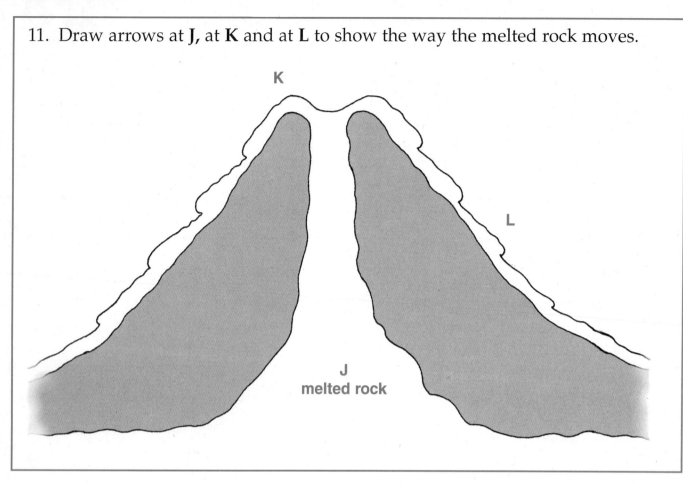

K

L

J
melted rock

12. What is a person doing when the person makes an object for the first time? _____

13. The person who makes an object for the first time is called an

_____.

14. The object the person makes is called an _____.

GO TO PART C IN YOUR TEXTBOOK.

Name _____

A Story Items

1. What was wrong with the waterbed that Grandmother Esther invented?

    _____

2. At first Leonard thought that he couldn't be an inventor because

    _____

    _____.

3. The first thing you do when you think like an inventor is find a

    _____.

4. What's the next thing you do?
    - Ask questions.
    - Meet the need.
    - Go to a museum.

5. Leonard's father had two ideas for inventions. One was something that cut down on traffic. What was his other idea?

    _____

6. Did Leonard's father think like an inventor? _____

7. Leonard's mother had an idea for an invention. What was it?

    _____

8. Had Grandmother Esther heard that idea before? _____

9. Did Grandmother Esther like that idea? _____

10. Did Leonard get any good ideas for inventions by talking to people?

    _____

11. What did Leonard think the hardest part of being an inventor was?

    _____

Review Items

12. How many Great Lakes are there? _____

13. Color the Great Lakes on the map.

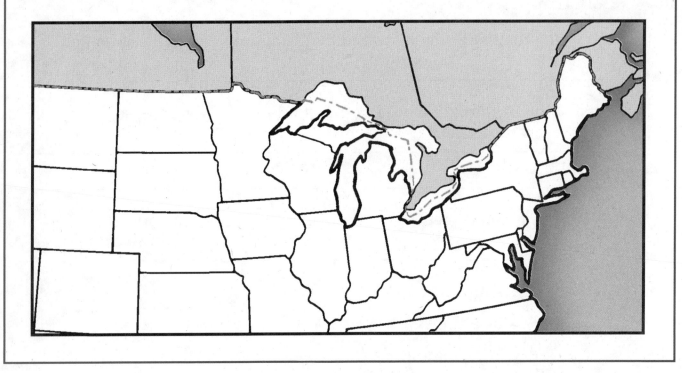

14. The picture below shows the sun and two balls. Fix up the balls so that half of each ball is in sunlight and half is in shadow.

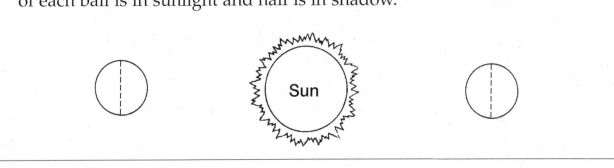

GO TO PART C IN YOUR TEXTBOOK.

Name _____

 Story Items

1. Leonard's mother had an idea for an invention. What was it?

    • a vacation that lasted all year long
    • an automatic grocery list writer
    • an automatic car washer

2. What did Leonard think the hardest part of being an inventor was?

    _____

3. Grandmother Esther told Leonard about 2 kind of dreams. **Underline** those 2 kinds of dreams.

    • the dreams of a butterfly   • silly wishes
    • the dreams of an inventor   • day dreams

4. Why was Leonard ready to give up trying to be an inventor?

    _____

5. Leonard discovered that he needed a shoe checker. How did he know about

    that need? _____

    _____

6. Is asking people about their needs the best way to get ideas for inventions?

    _____

7. The best way to think like an inventor is to do things. When you do things,

    you look for _____ that you have.

Review Items

8. In which direction do geese migrate in the fall? _____

9. In which direction do geese migrate in the spring? _____

10. Write the directions **north, south, east** and **west** in the boxes.

11. Make a line that starts at the circle on the map and goes north.

12. If you start at the circle and move to the number **4,** in which direction do you go? _____

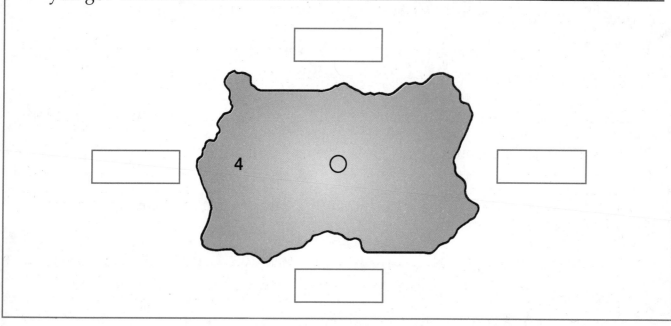

13. Shade the part of the earth where it is nighttime.

14. Which side of the earth is closer to the sun, **A** or **B?** _____

15. Which side of the earth is in nighttime? _____

16. Which side of the earth is in daytime? _____

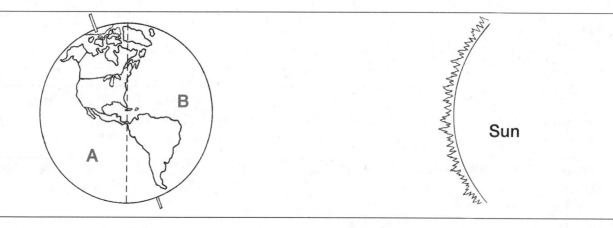

17. **Fill in the blanks to show the four seasons.**

winter, _____, summer, fall, _____,

spring, _____, _____

GO TO PART C IN YOUR TEXTBOOK.

Name _____

A Story Items

1. When Leonard did things like washing the car, what did he pay

   attention to? _____

2. Each problem told Leonard about something he could

   _____ to solve the problem.

3. How long did Leonard try to find different problems?

   _____

4. What invention did he think would solve the problem he had with

   eggs? _____

5. What problem did Leonard have with his clothes at bedtime?

   _____

6. What invention did he think could solve that problem?

   _____

7. What invention did Leonard think could solve the problem he had

   when it rained? _____

8. What problem did Leonard have when he washed his dog?

   _____

9. Which invention did Leonard's mother think he should make?

   _____

10. Did Grandmother Esther name an invention that Leonard should

    make? _____

Review Items

Use these names to answer the questions: **Tyrannosaurus, Triceratops.**

11. What is animal A? _____

12. What is animal B? _____

A   B

13. The first thing you do when you think like an inventor is find a _____.

14. What's the next thing you do? _____

_____

15. Write **north, south, east** and **west** in the correct boxes.

16. In which direction is ocean current **W** moving? _____

17. In which direction is ocean current **X** moving? _____

18. Which direction is the wind coming from? _____

19. Make an arrow above ice chunk **Y** to show the direction the current will move the ice chunk.

20. Make an arrow next to ice chunk **Z** to show the direction the current will move the ice chunk.

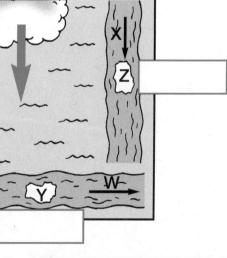

GO TO PART C IN YOUR TEXTBOOK.

Name _____

A Story Items

1. Underline the reasons that people on the street thought Grandmother Esther was mad at Leonard.

   - She made faces.
   - She pointed her finger.
   - She talked softly.
   - She talked loudly.
   - She kicked cats.

2. What invention did Leonard think could make his grandmother talk in a softer voice? _____

3. What would the invention do when Grandmother Esther talked louder?

   _____

Grandmother Esther explained how the electric eye works.

4. When somebody walks in the door, the body stops the beam of light from reaching the _____.

5. When the body stops the beam, what happens?

   _____

   _____

6. What does that tell the shopkeeper? _____

   _____

7. Why couldn't the people get into the bakery while Grandmother Esther talked? _____

   _____

8. What did those people say about Grandmother Esther's talk?

_____

9. How did Leonard feel? _____

10. Will the buzzer in the bakery make noise for picture **A** or picture **B?** _____

11. What's the name of the invention shown in the pictures?

_____

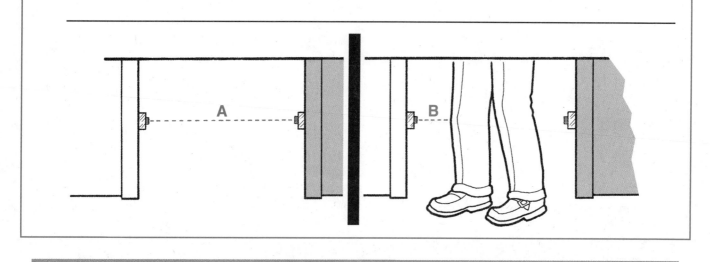

Review Items

12. What color are all geese when they are born? _____

13. What's the name of geese that are all white? _____

14. What's the name of geese that are gray and white and black? _____

GO TO PART C IN YOUR TEXTBOOK.

Name _____

A Story Items

1. Leonard got his idea for a great invention when Grandmother Esther told him to do something. What did she tell him to do?

_____

Leonard's original invention had problems.

2. What does the light in a dark room do when you walk into the room?

_____

3. What does the light do when you leave the room?

_____

4. Let's say two people walk into a dark room. What happens to the light in the room when the first person enters?

_____

5. What happens to the light when the second person enters?

_____

6. What will Leonard use to make the lights work automatically?

_____

7. Did Leonard's mother understand how his invention would work?

_____

8. Grandmother Esther told Leonard that every invention has

_____

9. So what does the inventor have to do?

        • quit   • solve the problems   • hide the problems

Here's the rule about an electric eye: **Each time the beam of light is broken, the light changes.** Shade the bulbs that are off for each problem. The first problem is already done for you.

10. The light is off. The beam is broken 4 times.

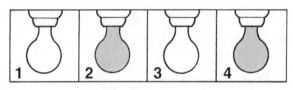

Is the light **on** or **off** at the end? _____

11. Here's another problem. The light is off. The beam is broken 8 times.

a. Shade the bulbs that are off.

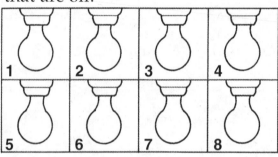

b. Is the light **on** or **off** at the end? _____

12. Here's another problem. The light is off. The beam is broken 3 times.

a. Shade the bulbs that are off.

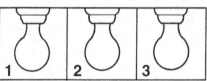

b. Is the light **on** or **off** at the end? _____

GO TO PART C IN YOUR TEXTBOOK.

Name _____

A **Story Items**

1. At the beginning of today's story, Leonard was trying to solve this problem: When a second person goes into the room, ████ .

   • the lights go on   • the lights stay on   • the lights go off

2. Leonard saw a sign that gave him a clue about solving his problem. What kind of sign did he see?

   _____

3. His invention had to know whether a person was moving ████ .

   • in or out   • fast or slow   • now or later

4. So how many beams does a doorway need? _____

5. If a person moves **into** the room, which beam will be broken first—the **inside beam** or the **outside beam?** _____

6. Which beam will be broken next? _____

7. Will the lights turn **on** or **off?** _____

8. The picture shows two electric eye beams on the side of each door. The number **1** shows the beam that is broken first. The number **2** shows the beam that is broken next. On each picture, draw an arrow to show which way the person is moving. The first arrow is already drawn.

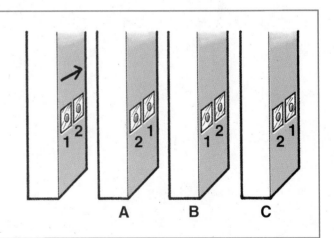

A   B   C

Here's the rule about an electric eye: **Each time the beam of light is broken, the light changes.**

9. a. The light is off. The beam is broken 3 times. Shade the bulbs that are off.

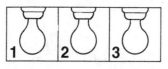

   b. Is the light **on** or **off** at the end? _____

10. a. The light is off. The beam is broken 6 times. Shade the bulbs that are off.

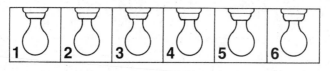

   b. Is the light **on** or **off** at the end? _____

11. a. The light is off. The beam is broken 5 times. Shade the bulbs that are off.

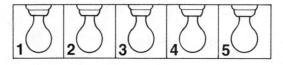

   b. Is the light **on** or **off** at the end? _____

GO TO PART C IN YOUR TEXTBOOK.

Name _____

A Story Items

1. In the last story, Leonard saw a sign that gave him a clue about solving his problem. What kind of sign did he see?

    _____

2. Would a person be moving into the room or out of the room if the **inside**

    beam is broken first? _____

3. Which way would a person be moving if the **outside** beam was broken first?

    _____

4. Leonard's original idea had a problem. What would happen if three people were in a room and one person left?

    _____

5. Grandmother Esther told Leonard that his device could not

    _____.

6. Letting water out of the sink gave Leonard an idea about his counter. What

    number did his counter have to count to? _____

7. Every time somebody goes into the room, what does the counter do?

    • + 1   • − 1   • − 0

8. Every time somebody goes out of the room, what does the counter do?

    • + 1   • − 1   • − 0

9. What number does the counter end up at when the last person leaves the

    room? _____

10. What happens to the lights when the counter is at zero?

    _____

The solid arrows show people going into the room. The dotted arrows show people leaving the room. For each picture, **underline** the word that tells about the lights in the room.

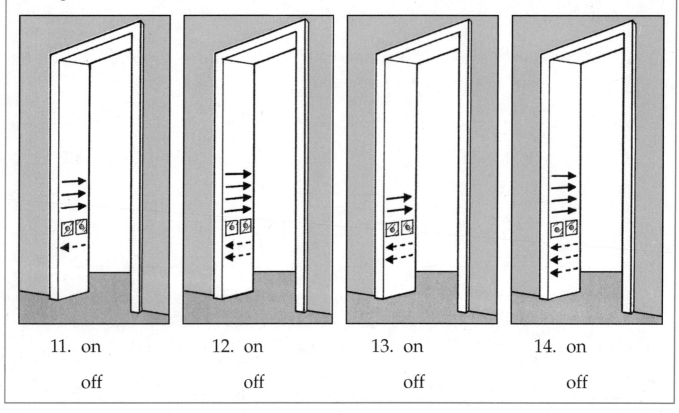

11. on

   off

12. on

   off

13. on

   off

14. on

GO TO PART C IN YOUR TEXTBOOK.

Name _____

A Story Items

Answer these questions about Leonard's invention.

1. What runs the electric eye?

    • city   • electricity   • grandmothers

2. What will run the counter? _____

3. Name 3 things Grandmother Esther does that are unusual for a

    grandmother. _____

    _____

4. Who paid for the electrical supplies? _____

5. How much did they cost? _____

6. The model had a little doorway that was about ▮▮▮ tall.

    • 2 feet   • 1 meter   • 1 centimeter

7. There was a _____ connected to the top.

8. The light is off. A doll goes through the doorway. What happens to the
    light if the outside beam is broken first?

    _____

9. Did Leonard's device work? _____

10. Did he test it more than 1 time? _____

11. What does an inventor get to protect an invention?

    _____

12. If other people want to make copies of an invention, they have to

    make a deal with the _____.

13. What does the inventor usually make those people do?

    _____

14. Special lawyers who get protection for inventions are called ▮▮▮.

        • patents   • doctors   • patent attorneys

15. How many meetings did Leonard and Grandmother Esther have with a

    special lawyer? _____

16. How much money did Grandmother Esther pay the lawyer?

    • 3 thousand dollars   • 3 hundred dollars   • 1 thousand dollars

Review Items

Use these names to answer the questions: **Tyrannosaurus, Triceratops.**

17. What is animal P? _____

18. What is animal J? _____

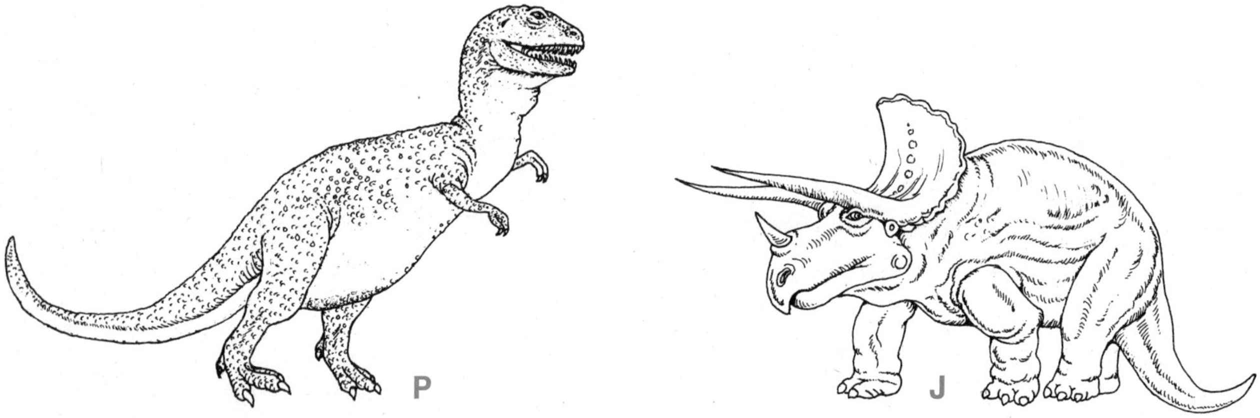

GO TO PART C IN YOUR TEXTBOOK.

Name _____

A Story Items

1. On which table would Leonard set up his display? _____

Look at the picture below. Not all the spaces have numbers and letters.

2. **Fill in the letters** that go at the top of each aisle.
3. **Number** all the tables in the aisle where Leonard's display was.
4. **Circle** Leonard's table.
5. Leonard and his grandmother started where the **X** is. They first went across the hall to the correct aisle. Then they walked down that aisle to their table. **Draw a path** that shows how they went from the **X** to their table.

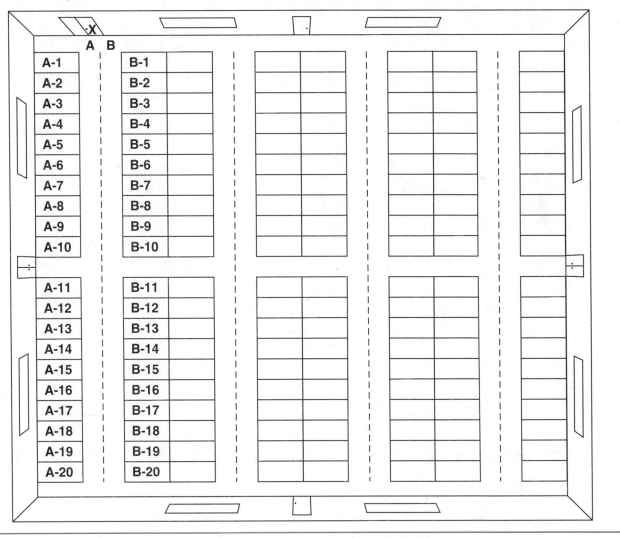

6. **Circle** Leonard's table.

7. What space is just north of Leonard's space? _____

8. What space is just west of Leonard's space? _____

9. What space is just south of Leonard's space? _____

10. What space is just east of Leonard's space? _____

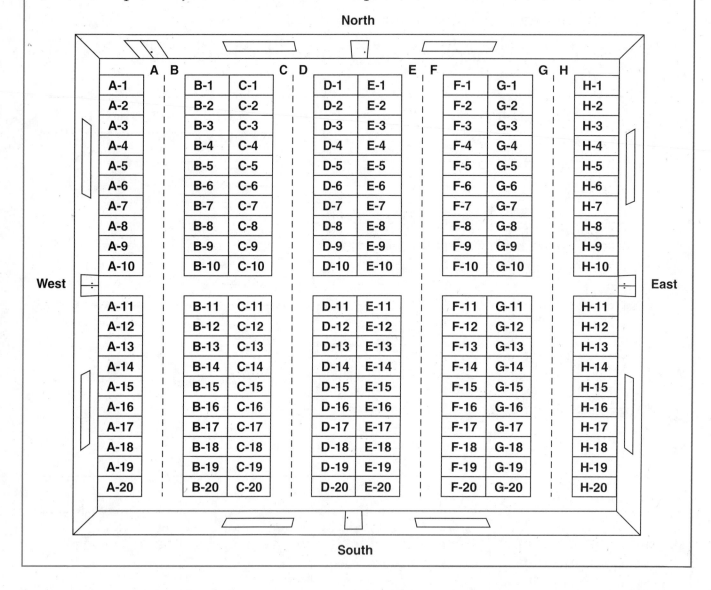

GO TO PART C IN YOUR TEXTBOOK.

86   *Lesson 47*

Name _____

A Story Items

1. Leonard was very disappointed when the fair opened. Tell why.

    • Lots of manufacturers showed up.
    • Not many people showed up.
    • Grandmother Esther talked too much.

2. How many people stopped at Leonard's display the first afternoon?

    _____

3. How many of them seemed very interested? _____

4. Why don't smart manufacturers act interested in the inventions that they want?

    • so they don't have to pay as much for the invention
    • because they are at the fair all day long
    • because they want to pay more for the invention

5. After supper, there were great crowds of people at the fair. Were these people

    manufacturers? _____

6. Did these people act interested in Leonard's invention? _____

7. Name 2 things that make you think the slim woman in the gray coat was a manufacturer.

    _____

    _____

8. Why would manufacturers want to make their deals before the prizes are announced?

    • so they could go home earlier
    • so they wouldn't have to pay as much
    • so they had something to do

9. Grandmother Esther gave 2 reasons that the manufacturers did not wait until the afternoon to make their deals. What are those 2 reasons?

_____

_____

Look at the picture below.
10. Make an **I** by each inventor.
11. Make an **M** by each manufacturer.

GO TO PART C IN YOUR TEXTBOOK.

Name _____

A **Story Items**

1. Leonard was very disappointed when the invention fair opened. Tell why.

_____

2. Grandmother Esther gave 2 reasons that the manufacturers did
not wait until Saturday afternoon to make their deals. What are those 2
reasons?

_____

_____

Look at the list of deals below.
3. **Underline** the best deal for an inventor.
4. **Circle** the best deal for a manufacturer.

   • 18 thousand dollars and 6 dollars for every copy sold
   • 12 thousand dollars and 6 dollars for every copy sold
   • 17 thousand dollars and 6 dollars for every copy sold

5. The slim woman in the gray coat said that not many people would be
interested in Leonard's invention. Does she really think that?

_____

6. Why did she say it?

   • She didn't want to talk to her boss.
   • She didn't want to pay a lot for the invention.
   • She didn't like the invention.

7. Why didn't Grandmother Esther want Leonard to make any deals?

   • because he didn't know how
   • because he was too young
   • because he was too tired

8. The man with the slim woman wanted to make his company sound good to Leonard and Grandmother Esther. Tell why.

_____

_____

_____

9. Did his talk trick Grandmother Esther? _____

10. Which prize did Grandmother Esther think Leonard's invention would get?

_____

11. Let's say a manufacturer had not made a deal for an invention. Which would the manufacturer have to pay more money for, an invention that won a prize or an invention that did not win a prize?

_____

12. What lie did Grandmother Esther tell the bald man?
    - ABC Home Products is not interested.
    - ABC Home Products wants to make a deal.
    - ABC Home Products has too many inventions.

13. When Grandmother Esther told a lie, Leonard was going to remind her that

ABC Home Products _____

_____.

GO TO PART C IN YOUR TEXTBOOK.

90   *Lesson 49*

51

Name _____

A **Story Items**

1. The slim woman in the gray coat said that not many people would be interested in Leonard's invention. Did she really think that? _____

2. Why did she say it?
    - She didn't like the invention.
    - She didn't want to talk to her boss.
    - She didn't want to pay a lot for the invention.

3. The woman in the gray coat made two offers. Tell about her **first** offer.

    _____ dollars for the invention and

    _____ for every copy that is sold.

4. Did Leonard like that offer? _____

5. Did Grandmother Esther like that offer? _____

6. Tell about the offer everyone agreed on.

    _____ dollars for the invention and

    _____ for every copy that is sold.

7. **Underline** the 2 ways that tell how the slim woman changed after she made the deal.

    - Her voice was pleasant.   - Her voice was loud.
    - She smiled.   - Her voice was higher.
    - She yelled.   - She closed her eyes.

8. What did Grandmother Esther and Leonard have to do to finish the deal?
    - win a prize
    - get another patent
    - sign papers

9. Who did Grandmother Esther think would win first prize?

_____

10. Who won first prize? _____

11. What was the person's invention? _____

_____

12. How much money did Leonard win for his prize?

_____

13. Why did Leonard want Grandmother Esther to go on the stage with him?
    - She wanted to go up there.
    - She helped with his invention.
    - She knew Ronald Hogan.

14. Did she want to do that? _____

Review Item

15. The picture shows the sun and two balls. Fix up the balls so that half of each ball is in sunlight and half is in shadow.

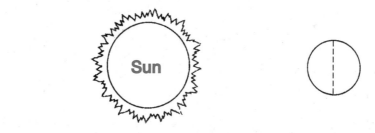

■■■■■■■■■■■ **GO TO PART C IN YOUR TEXTBOOK.** ■■■■■■■■

92   *Lesson 51*

52

Name ______________________________

A Story Items

1. The woman in the gray coat made two offers. Her first offer was ______________________ dollars for the invention and ______________________ for every copy that is sold.
2. Did Leonard like that offer? ______________________
3. Did Grandmother Esther like that offer? ______________________
4. The offer that everyone agreed on was ______________________ dollars for the invention and ______________________ for every copy that is sold.
5. Name one reason Leonard didn't have much free time anymore.

   ____
6. What name did ABC Home Products give to Leonard's invention?

   ____

Answer these questions about the ad:

7. The ad said you should put a light saver in ______________________ of your house.
8. Who should you see about getting some light savers? ______________________
9. Leonard's mother solved one problem she had with grocery shopping. She solved that problem by buying ______.
   - a grocery cart
   - a Mr. Light Saver
   - an automatic list-writer
10. Leonard's mother still had a problem when she went grocery shopping. What was her problem?
    - opening the trunk while holding groceries
    - turning on lights while holding groceries
    - holding groceries and playing the drums

GO TO PART D IN YOUR TEXTBOOK.

Use the picture below and your lined paper to explain how Leonard's new invention works. Your group may make arrows on the picture to show which parts will move. Your group may use dotted lines and words to name the parts or show how the parts of the invention work. Don't be afraid to write on the picture.

Then use lined paper to **tell** how your group's invention will work. Try to think about the different problems that there might be with the invention. Talk about these problems. Try to solve the problems. When you're finished, have someone from your group read your report to the class.

Name _____

A

1. How many suns are in the solar system? _____

2. How many planets are in the solar system? _____

3. Name the planet we live on. _____

4. What's in the middle of the solar system? _____

5. Name the only part of the solar system that's burning.

    • our moon   • Earth   • the sun

6. Is Earth the planet that is closest to the sun? _____

7. The sun gives _____ and _____ to all the planets.

8. Make an **X** on the sun.
9. Make a **Y** on Earth.

10. The planets are named below with Mercury first and Venus second. **Fill in the names of the missing planets.**

Mercury, Venus, _____, Mars, _____,

Saturn, _____, Neptune, _____.

11. Which planet is largest? _____

12. Which planet is next-largest? _____

13. How many times larger than Earth is the sun?

    • one hundred   • one thousand   • ten thousand

 Story Items

14. Does today's story take place in the past, the present, or the future?

    _____

15. Students who do well on the test will go on a trip. Where will they go?

    _____

16. About how many students are taking the test with Wendy?

    _____

17. How many students will go on the trip? _____

18. What country are those students from? _____

19. How long will the test take? _____

20. Why did Wendy feel sick at the end of the story? _____

    _____

    _____

GO TO PART D IN YOUR TEXTBOOK.

Name _____

A

1. Write the present year on line C.

2. Then write **past** or **future** next to each of the other years.

3. Write any **3** years that are in the past.

   _____

   _____

   _____

4. Write any **3** years that are in the future.

   _____

   _____

   _____

A. _____ ● 2230

B. _____ ● 2020

C. _____ ● Present year

D. _____ ● 1900

E. _____ ● 1380

5. Things that have already happened are in the _____.

6. Things that are happening now are in the _____.

7. Things that will happen are in the _____.

B **Story Items**

8. How long is Traveler Four? _____

9. How many people are in the crew? _____

10. How many passengers does it hold? _____

11. How fast can it travel? _____

12. How far is it from Earth to Jupiter?

    • 200 million miles   • 400 thousand miles   • 400 million miles

13. Here's a picture of Traveler Four. Label the lettered parts.

A _____   B _____ section

C _____ section   D _____ section

14. Which planet did Wendy know the most about? _____

15. Which planet did she find the most interesting? _____

16. Why did she think that planet was the most interesting? _____

_____

Review Items

17. The planets are named below with Mercury first and Venus second.
    Write the names of the missing planets.

    Mercury, Venus, Earth, _____, Jupiter,

    _____, Uranus, _____, Pluto.

GO TO PART D IN YOUR TEXTBOOK.

Name _____

A   **Story Items**

Answer these questions about Traveler Four.

1. How many people are in the crew? _____

2. How many passengers does it hold? _____

3. How fast can it travel? _____

4. How long did the test take? _____

5. Was Wendy sure that she had answered all the questions correctly?

    _____

6. Name all the Travelers that were earlier than Traveler Four.

    _____

7. How fast could Traveler One go? _____

8. The woman told the students how they would find out whether they would

    go on the trip. How would they find out? _____

    _____

9. Write the first name of the girl who sat behind Wendy during the test.

    _____

10. Did that girl think she did well on the test? _____

11. What did Wendy do after math class every day?

    _____

12. Was Wendy selected for the trip? _____

13. What planet will she go to? _____

Review Items

14. Name the planet we live on. _____

15. What's in the middle of the solar system? _____

16. Name the only part of the solar system that's burning. _____

17. Which planet is largest? _____

18. Which planet is next-largest? _____

19. How many moons does Jupiter have? _____

20. How many moons does Saturn have? _____

21. How far is it from Earth to Jupiter?

   • 400 miles   • 400 million miles   • 400 thousand miles

22. The picture shows half a hailstone. How many times did the stone go through a cloud? _____

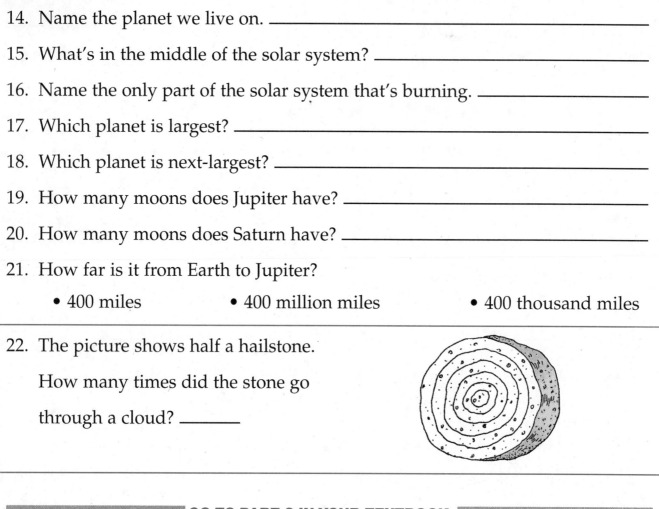

GO TO PART C IN YOUR TEXTBOOK.

Name _____

A

1. Which letter shows where Wendy's flight began? _____

2. Which letter shows Tokyo? _____

3. Draw a line to show the route that Wendy's jet plane took.

4. What's the largest city in Japan? _____

5. In which direction did the jet fly from Canada to Tokyo? _____

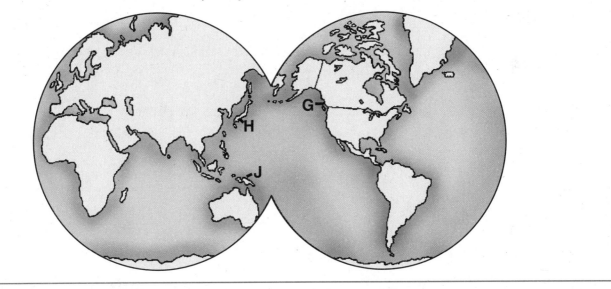

B **Story Items**

6. What city could Wendy see from the space station? _____

7. What country is that city in? _____

8. What country did Wendy's jet come from? _____

9. What was Wendy's weight limit for her baggage?

   • 40 pounds   • 100 pounds   • 140 pounds

10. Was Wendy in good health? _____

11. What surprise did Wendy have at the space station?

    _____

12. Was Sidney's name on the list of students who were going on the trip?

    _____

13. Why did Sidney get to go on the trip?

    _____

14. Most of the other passengers were not students. Who were they?

    _____

Review Items

15. The planets are named below with Mercury first and Venus second.
    Write the names of the missing planets.

    Mercury, Venus, Earth, _____, Jupiter,

    _____, Uranus, _____, Pluto.

16. How many moons does Jupiter have? _____

17. How many moons does Saturn have? _____

18. How far is it from Earth to Jupiter?

    • 800 million miles   • 40 million miles   • 400 million miles

19. If other people want to make copies of an invention, they have to make a

    deal with the _____.

20. What does the inventor usually make those people do?

    _____

▌GO TO PART D IN YOUR TEXTBOOK. ▌

102   *Lesson 56*

Name _____

 A **Story Items**

1. **Underline 5** things that were in the cabinet in front of Wendy's seat.

   - space books
   - space helmet
   - space suit
   - space food
   - bed
   - plates
   - writing table
   - TV screen
   - keyboard

2. Why would everybody need tanks of oxygen when they got to Jupiter?

   _____

   _____

3. How far back did the passengers have to move their seats before they

   took off? _____

4. What was Wendy's idea about why the ship was shaking?

   - It was speeding through layers of air.
   - It was falling apart.
   - It was too old.
   - It was too heavy.

5. The pressure on Wendy felt like a _____ sitting on her chest.

6. In what part of the spaceship were the engines?

   _____

7. The sound of the engines couldn't reach the passenger section because the

   spaceship _____

   _____

8. What planet did Wendy see when she looked out the window?

   _____

9. Make an **X** on a passenger seat.

10. Make a **P** on the space suit.

11. Make an **H** on the space helmet.

12. Make a **T** on the computer keyboard.

13. Make an **R** on the writing table.

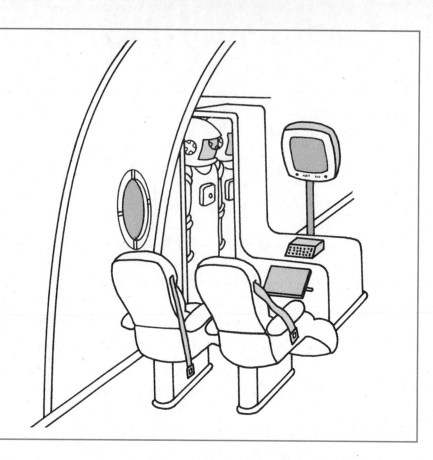

14. What planet is shown in the picture? _____

15. Write **N** on the part of the planet that has night.

16. Write **D** on the part of the planet that has daylight.

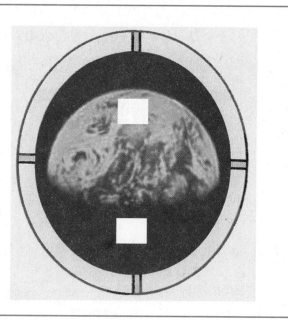

GO TO PART C IN YOUR TEXTBOOK.

Name _____

A

1. Gravity is the force that _____.

2. If something weighed 100 pounds on Earth, how many pounds would it weigh on the moon? _____

3. If something weighed 20 pounds on Earth, would it weigh more than 20 pounds on Saturn? _____

4. Would it weigh more than 20 pounds on the moon? _____

5. A person weighs 100 pounds on planet A and 300 pounds on planet B. Which planet has stronger gravity? _____

6. A person weighs 100 pounds on planet A and 90 pounds on planet B. Which planet has stronger gravity? _____

7. Planet A has weaker gravity than planet M. On which of those planets would you weigh more? _____

8. Which planets have stronger gravity, the **bigger** planets or the **smaller** ones?

_____

B **Story Items**

9. Why did Earth seem to get smaller? _____

_____

10. What makes the sky around Earth look blue?

• a layer of air   • the sun   • a layer of clouds

11. The pilot turned off the engines when the ship was out in space. Did the spaceship slow down? _____

12. Was there any air outside the spaceship? _____

13. What happens to people and things when there's no gravity?

    • They drop.   • They float.   • They survive.

14. When the gravity device is turned on, do things float in the air or fall to the floor? _____

15. The gravity device is off. What would happen if you hit a **big** blob of floating liquid? _____

    _____

16. Do things fall to the floor when the gravity device is off? _____

17. Did the gravity device come back on **fast** or **slowly?** _____

18. If you drop something on Earth, it falls to the ground. What makes it fall?

    _____

Review Item

19. **Fill in the blanks to show the four seasons.**

    winter, _____, summer, fall, _____,

    spring, _____, _____

GO TO PART D IN YOUR TEXTBOOK.

Name ______________________________

A **Story Items**

1. Traveler Four had gone over 40 million miles in less than ______.
   - 1 hour
   - 11 hours
   - 1 day

Answer these questions about Earth and Mars.

2. Which planet has more clouds around it? ______________________
3. Which planet is smaller? ______________________
4. Which planet is colder? ______________________
5. Why is that planet colder? ______________________

   ____

6. Did Wendy sleep well during the first night on the spaceship? __________
7. Why did the sun seem to be getting smaller? ______________________

   ____

8. Everyone needed to do exercises so they wouldn't get ______________.
9. Name **2** of the exercises they did. ______________________

   ____

10. How did Wendy sleep the second night? ______________________
11. What planet did everyone see on the next day? ______________________
12. What did the pilot do to the spaceship? ______________________

    ____

13. How many moons of Jupiter could Wendy see? ______________________
14. How many moons does Jupiter have altogether? ______________________
15. Which planet has more moons, Saturn or Jupiter? ______________________

16. **Underline** the 5 things that tell how Jupiter looked to Wendy.

- It was small.
- It was green and blue.
- It was beautiful.
- It had stripes.

- She could see four moons.
- It was huge.
- She could see twelve moons.
- It was brown, orange and white.

Review Items

17. In which direction do geese migrate in the fall? _____

18. In which direction do geese migrate in the spring? _____

19. Write the directions **north, south, east** and **west** in the boxes.

20. Make a line that starts at the circle on the map and goes north.

21. If you start at the circle and move to the number 6, in which direction do

    you go? _____

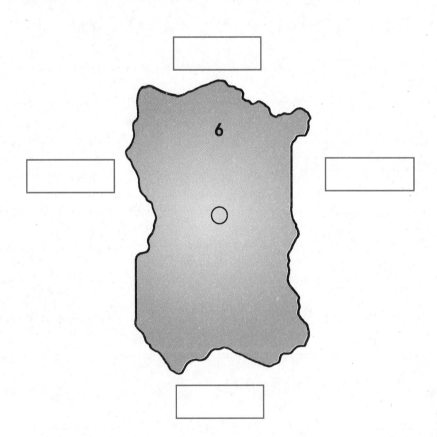

GO TO PART C IN YOUR TEXTBOOK.

108   *Lesson 59*

Name _____

A Story Items

1. How much oxygen is on Io? _____

2. What must people wear so they can breathe on Io?

   _____

3. The automatic radio in the space suit tells people how to get back to the

   _____ and how

   much _____ they have left.

4. How well did Wendy sleep on the last night? _____

5. Name the moon where the ship will land. _____

6. What makes it dark on the surface of Jupiter?

   _____

7. Could you see very far on Jupiter with bright lights? _____

8. Do gases surround Io? _____

9. Does Io move around Jupiter **fast** or **slowly?** _____

10. It takes Io about _____ to go all the way around Jupiter.

11. Where did the passengers keep their space suits? _____

    _____

12. The passengers tried on their space suits. Did the space suits feel **heavy** or

    light? _____

13. Would they feel that way on Io? _____

14. Tell why. _____

    _____

15. Why did the engines of the spaceship start up again?
- to slow the ship down
- to speed the ship up
- to turn in circles

16. What planet is shown?

_____

17. Make an **X** on the "eye" of the planet.

18. Which is bigger, the "eye" or

Earth? _____

19. The planets are named below with Mercury first. **Write the names of the missing planets.**

Mercury, _____, Earth, _____, Jupiter,

_____, Uranus, _____, Pluto.

GO TO PART C IN YOUR TEXTBOOK.

Name _____

A Story Items

1. As Traveler Four approached Io, the engines came on with great force.

    Tell why. _____

    _____

2. Did Wendy **feel** the engines or **hear** the engines?

    _____

3. Why were the passengers glad to leave the spaceship?

    _____

4. Did Wendy feel **light** or **heavy** when she left the ship?

    _____

5. Tell why.

    • Io has weaker gravity.
    • Io has stronger gravity.
    • Io has no oxygen.

6. Wendy jumped 5 feet high. Could she jump that high on Earth? _____

7. Tell about the size of Wendy's room. _____

    _____

8. Name 2 things that were in the room. _____

9. There were maps and lots of other things at the space station to teach

    visitors about Jupiter. Name 2 other things. _____

    _____

10. How big is Jupiter compared to the other planets in the solar system?

    • bigger   • smaller   • the same size

11. How long does it take Jupiter to spin around one time?

    _____

12. What place on Io did Wendy and Sidney want to visit?

    _____

13. How far from the space station was the volcano?

    • 30 miles   • half a mile   • 100 meters

Review Items

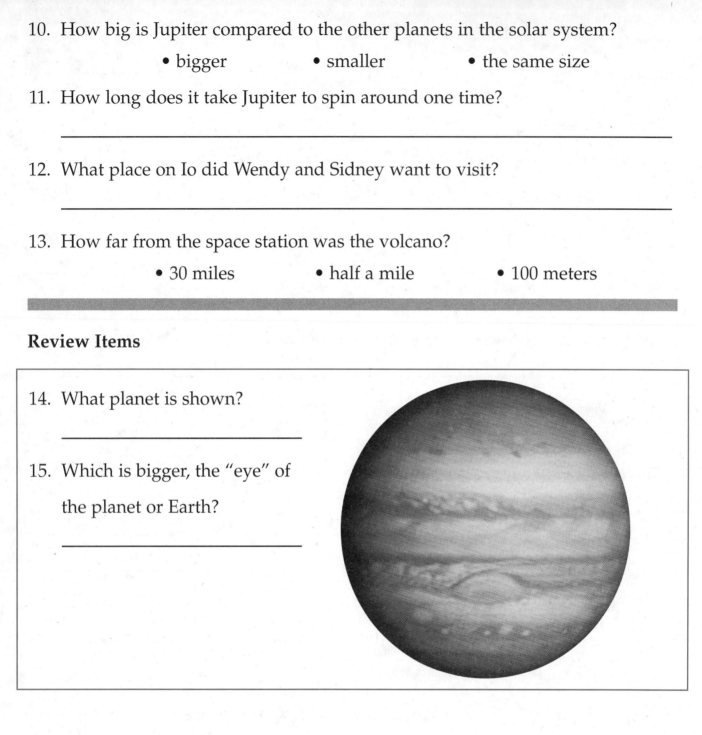

14. What planet is shown?

    _____

15. Which is bigger, the "eye" of
    the planet or Earth?

    _____

GO TO PART D IN YOUR TEXTBOOK.

Name _____

A Story Items

1. What was the temperature outside the space station?

   _____

2. Did it feel cold to Wendy? _____

3. Tell why. _____

   _____

4. Wendy and Sidney were running and leaping when they first left the space station. The automatic radio told Wendy if she kept doing what she was doing, she would run out of oxygen in ▮▮▮ .

   • 5 minutes   • 35 minutes   • 25 minutes

5. Which uses up more oxygen, **walking** or **running?** _____

6. The girls were heading toward the volcano. What marked the path?

   _____

7. What's another name for hot melted rock? _____

8. What name did the volcano have? _____

9. What color is lava when it's very hot? _____

10. What color is lava after it cools a little bit? _____

11. What color is lava after it's completely cooled? _____

12. The inside of the volcano was larger than a _____ .

13. As the girls started to walk around the rim of the volcano, the voice came over Wendy's radio again. How long would Wendy's oxygen last if she kept using it as fast as she had been using it?

   • 45 minutes   • 35 minutes   • 25 minutes

14. What did the girls walk onto to look down into the volcano?

　　　　　• a sidewalk　　　　• an overhang　　　　• a slide

15. What happened while they were standing on it?

_____

16. What did Wendy grab? _____

17. What happened to Sidney? _____

_____

Review Items

18. Which planet in the picture has more gravity? _____

19. How do you know? _____

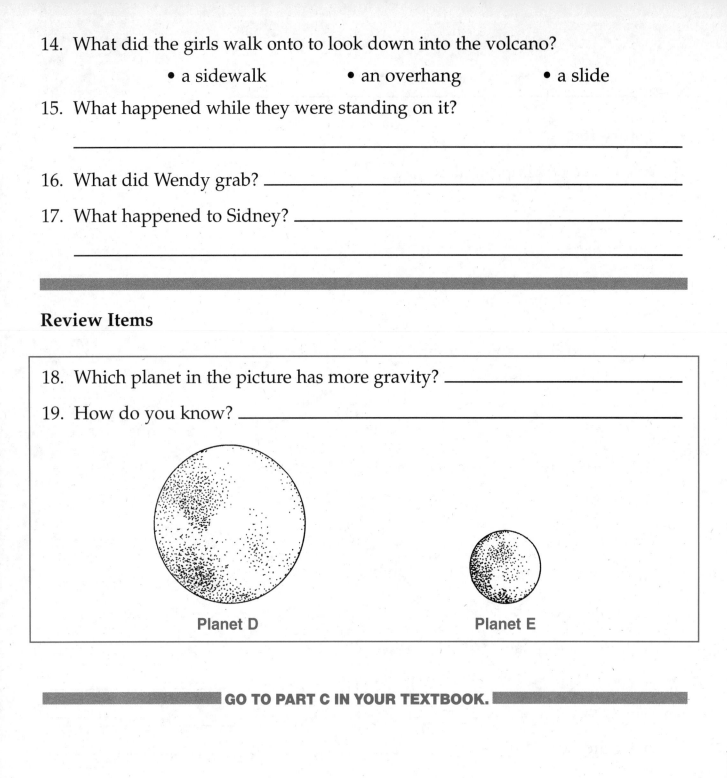

Planet D　　　　　　　　　　　　Planet E

GO TO PART C IN YOUR TEXTBOOK.

Name _____

A Story Items

1. After the overhang fell, Wendy pulled herself up onto the rim of the volcano.

   Was this **hard** or **easy?** _____

2. Tell why.

   - The gravity was weak.
   - There wasn't any oxygen.
   - She was in a space suit.

3. Was Sidney in the lava? _____

4. How close were Sidney's feet to the lava?

   _____

5. Where did Wendy go to get help for Sidney?

   _____

6. On the way to get help, the automatic voice came over Wendy's radio. Why?

   - She was using up oxygen too fast.
   - She was not running fast enough.
   - Her space suit was getting too hot.

7. Whose voice came over Wendy's radio next? _____

8. What did he tell her to do? _____

9. Wendy ran out of oxygen. **Underline 3** things that happened to Wendy.

   - Her arms became stiff.
   - Her arms became tingly.
   - Her voice wouldn't work.
   - Her voice was loud.
   - She saw Rod.
   - She saw spots.

10. About how far from the space station was Wendy when she passed out?

    - 200 centimeters
    - 10 yards
    - 200 meters

11. Where was Wendy when she woke up? _____

12. How many people were in the vehicle with Wendy? _____

13. Who was driving? _____

14. What did the woman attach to Wendy's space suit?

_____

15. Where did the vehicle stop? _____

Review Items

Here's the rule about an electric eye: **Each time the beam of light is broken, the light changes.**

16. The light is off. The beam is broken 4 times. Shade the bulbs that are off.

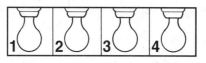

17. Is the light **on** or **off** at the end? _____

18. The light is off. The beam is broken 3 times. Shade the bulbs that are off.

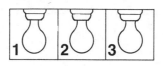

19. Is the light **on** or **off** at the end? _____

20. The light is off. The beam is broken 6 times. Shade the bulbs that are off.

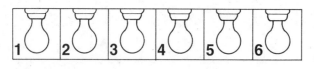

21. Is the light **on** or **off** at the end? _____

GO TO PART C IN YOUR TEXTBOOK.

Name _____

A **Story Items**

1. What was Sidney hanging on to when Wendy left for help?

   _____

2. Where was Sidney when Wendy came back?

   _____

3. What did Wendy think had happened to Sidney?

   _____

4. What happened to the end of the rope that fell into the lava?

   _____

5. Who slid down the rope? _____

6. What did he tell Sidney to do? _____

   _____

7. When Sidney reached the top of the rim, how did she look?

   • healthy   • pale   • sad

8. Why could everybody take their helmets off inside the space station?

   _____

9. **Underline 2** words that tell how Sidney felt at the end of the story.

   • thirsty   • tired   • cold   • glad

Review Items

10. How many moons does Jupiter have? _____

11. Which planet has more moons, Saturn or Jupiter? _____

12. How much oxygen surrounds Io? _____

13. Does Io move around Jupiter **fast** or **slowly?** _____

14. It takes Io about _____ to go all the way around Jupiter.

15. Which planet in the picture has more gravity? _____

16. How do you know? _____

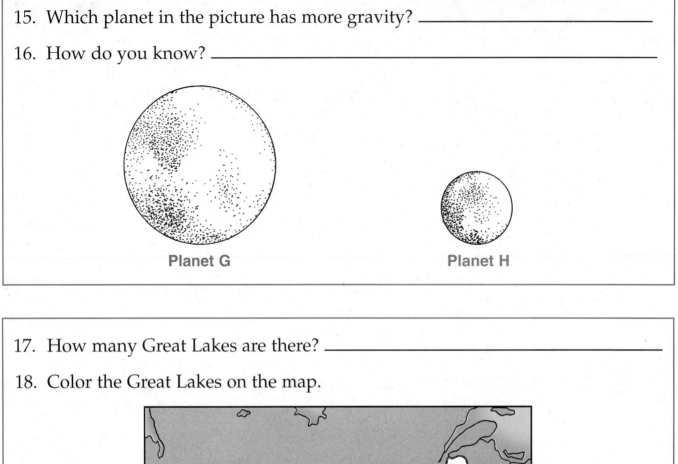

Planet G   Planet H

17. How many Great Lakes are there? _____

18. Color the Great Lakes on the map.

GO TO PART C IN YOUR TEXTBOOK.

Name _____

A Story Items

1. How long did the students stay on Io? _____

2. Name 3 things Wendy did after her adventure at Soup Pot.

   ❶ _____

   ❷ _____

   ❸ _____

3. When it was time to go back home to Earth, Wendy felt both happy and sad.

   She felt happy because she would see _____.

4. She felt sad because she would have to say goodbye to

   _____.

5. Wendy took lots of pictures of the things she saw. Which pictures did Wendy want more than all the rest?

   _____

6. How far away were the big volcanos the girls visited?

   • 200 miles   • 100 miles   • 1 mile

7. Name 2 ways these volcanos were different from Soup Pot.

   ❶ _____

   ❷ _____

8. Name 2 things Wendy planned to do when she got back to her home town.

   ❶ _____

   ❷ _____

9. What time of day was it when Traveler Four landed in Japan?

_____

10. Did Wendy and Sidney get on the same plane? _____

11. The woman sitting next to Wendy on the plane was reading a book. What

   was it about? _____

12. The woman asked about a place that made Wendy laugh. What place was
   that?

          • Jupiter   • Io   • Saturn

Review Items

13. Write the letter of the footprint made by the heaviest animal. _____

14. Write the letter of the footprint made by the lightest animal. _____

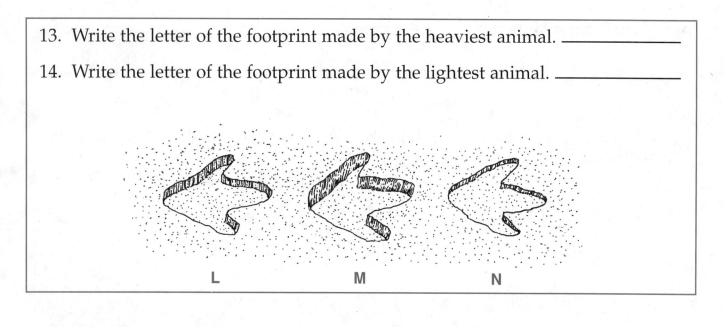

L   M   N

GO TO PART C IN YOUR TEXTBOOK.

Name _____

A

Here are animal names in alphabetical order. Label each animal in the picture below.

bear	giraffe	lion	sheep
cow	goat	parrot	squirrel
eagle	hamster	pigeon	tiger
elephant	horse	rabbit	zebra

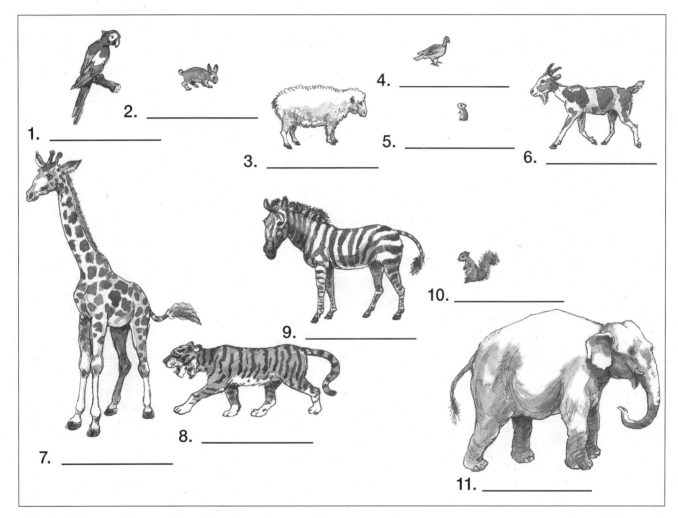

1. _____
2. _____
3. _____
4. _____
5. _____
6. _____
7. _____
8. _____
9. _____
10. _____
11. _____

12. Make an **X** on the elephant's trunk.

B   Story Items

13. How old was Waldo when he started cooking? _____

14. Did people like Waldo's cooking? _____

15. Who liked Waldo's cooking? _____

16. When the circus animals gathered in Waldo's yard, the weather was _____ and the windows were _____.

17. How did Waldo's family feel about having so many animals in the yard?

    _____

18. What did Waldo use to get the animals back into the truck? _____

19. Which animals did Waldo feed in the truck—the circus animals or the other animals? _____

20. What did Waldo do after the other animals followed him out of the truck?

    _____

21. Did the animals need to eat a lot of Waldo's food to make them happy?

    _____

22. When the trainer saw how Waldo handled the animals, they were ▮▮▮▮.
    - angry   - amazed   - tired

Review Item

23. Draw arrows at **X,** at **Y** and at **Z** to show the way the melted rock moves.

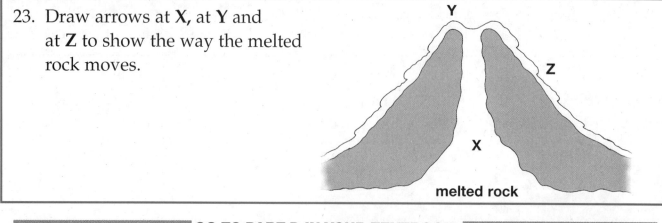

melted rock

GO TO PART D IN YOUR TEXTBOOK.

Name _____

A Story Items

1. Why did people stay in Waldo's yard after the circus animals left?

   _____

   _____

2. Why couldn't those people see Waldo's legs?

   _____

   _____

3. How did those people **feel** about the show the animals were putting on?

   _____

4. Why did people from all over make phone calls to Waldo's house?

   _____

5. Waldo's sister thought it was ridiculous when somebody asked her if she'd

   seen a striped cat. Why did she think it was ridiculous? _____

   _____

6. Waldo came up with a solution to solve a problem with his cooking. What

   was his solution? _____

7. Did his parents agree with his solution? _____

8. What decision did Waldo's parents make?

   _____

Review Items

9. Write **north, south, east** and **west** in the correct boxes.

10. In which direction is ocean current **R** moving? _____

11. In which direction is ocean current **S** moving? _____

12. Which direction is the wind coming from? _____

13. Make an arrow above ice chunk **T** to show the direction the current will move the ice chunk.

14. Make an arrow next to ice chunk **U** to show the direction the current will move the ice chunk.

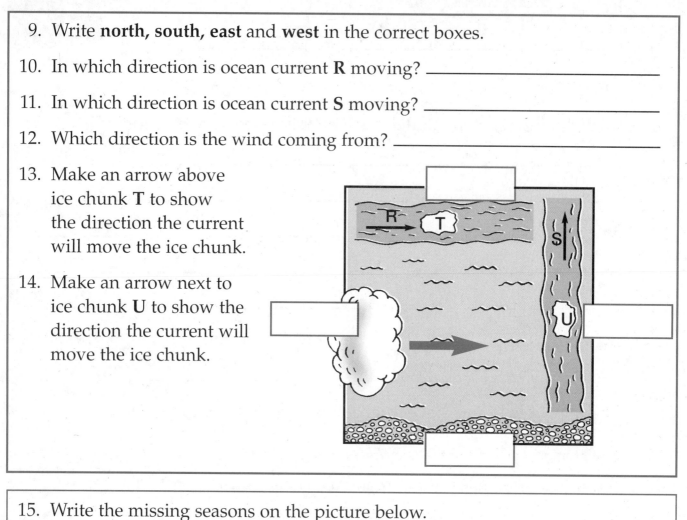

15. Write the missing seasons on the picture below.

16. Shade half of earth **J** and half of earth **L**.

M. _____

J. winter

Sun

L. _____

K. _____

GO TO PART C IN YOUR TEXTBOOK.

Name _____

A

1. When you're training an animal, what do you do each time the animal does

   the trick? _____

2. What do you do if the animal does not do the trick?

   _____

3. Name 2 things you could give to a dog to reward it.

   ❶ _____

   ❷ _____

B Story Items

4. Waldo's plan had two parts. First, Waldo was going to get _____.

5. Then he was going to fix up the _____.

6. What was the first job that Waldo got?

   _____

7. Why didn't he like that job? _____

   _____

8. What was the second job that Waldo got? _____

   _____

9. Why didn't he like that job? _____

   _____

10. What will Waldo do to make the animals in the pet shop happy?

    _____

11. While Waldo was cooking, the pet shop owner opened a window. Why did she do that?

_____

12. Why did Waldo tell her to close the window?

_____

Review Items

13. Shade the part of the earth where it is nighttime.

14. Which side of the earth is closer to the sun, **J** or **F**? _____

15. Which side of the earth is in nighttime? _____

16. Which side of the earth is in daytime? _____

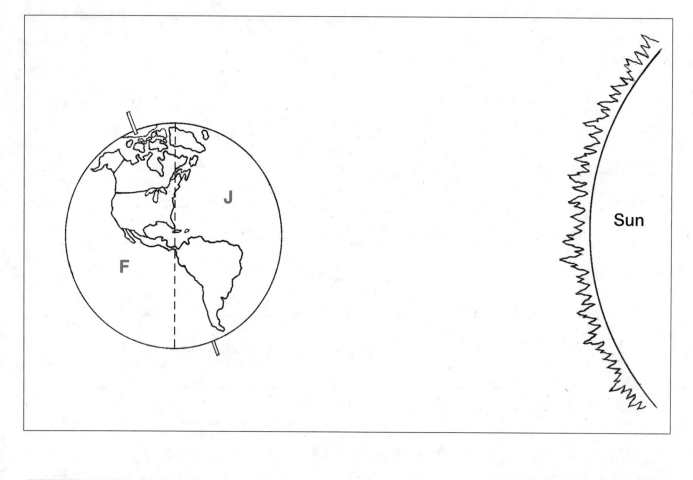

GO TO PART D IN YOUR TEXTBOOK.

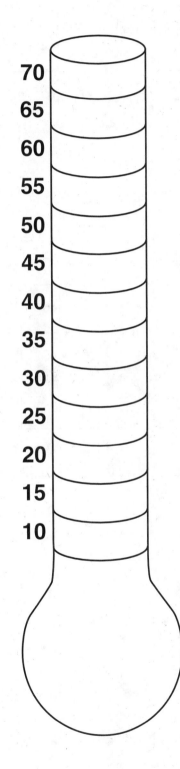

70

65

60

55

50

45

40

35

30

25

20

15

10

Fact Game Scorecards

Lesson 10

1	2	3	4	5
6	7	8	9	10
11	12	13	14	15
16	17	18	19	20

Lesson 20

1	2	3	4	5
6	7	8	9	10
11	12	13	14	15
16	17	18	19	20

Lesson 30

1	2	3	4	5
6	7	8	9	10
11	12	13	14	15
16	17	18	19	20

Lesson 40

1	2	3	4	5
6	7	8	9	10
11	12	13	14	15
16	17	18	19	20

Lesson 50

1	2	3	4	5
6	7	8	9	10
11	12	13	14	15
16	17	18	19	20

Lesson 60

1	2	3	4	5
6	7	8	9	10
11	12	13	14	15
16	17	18	19	20

Lesson 70

1	2	3	4	5
6	7	8	9	10
11	12	13	14	15
16	17	18	19	20